TEACHER'S GUIDE

Connected Mathematics 2 ™

What Do You Expect?

Probability and Expected Value

Glenda Lappan
James T. Fey
William M. Fitzgerald
Susan N. Friel
Elizabeth Difanis Phillips

PEARSON

Boston, Massachusetts · Glenview, Illinois · Shoreview, Minnesota · Upper Saddle River, New Jersey

Connected Mathematics™ was developed at Michigan State University with financial support from the Michigan State University Office of the Provost, Computing and Technology, and the College of Natural Science.

This material is based upon work supported by the National Science Foundation under Grant No. MDR 9150217 and Grant No. ESI 9986372. Opinions expressed are those of the authors and not necessarily those of the Foundation.

The Michigan State University authors and administration have agreed that all MSU royalties arising from this publication will be devoted to purposes supported by the Department of Mathematics and the MSU Mathematics Enrichment Fund.

13-digit ISBN 978-0-13-366199-6
10-digit ISBN 0-13-366199-7
1 2 3 4 5 6 7 8 9 10   11 10 09 08

Authors of Connected Mathematics

(from left to right) Glenda Lappan, Betty Phillips, Susan Friel, Bill Fitzgerald, Jim Fey

Glenda Lappan is a University Distinguished Professor in the Department of Mathematics at Michigan State University. Her research and development interests are in the connected areas of students' learning of mathematics and mathematics teachers' professional growth and change related to the development and enactment of K–12 curriculum materials.

James T. Fey is a Professor of Curriculum and Instruction and Mathematics at the University of Maryland. His consistent professional interest has been development and research focused on curriculum materials that engage middle and high school students in problem-based collaborative investigations of mathematical ideas and their applications.

William M. Fitzgerald (*Deceased*) was a Professor in the Department of Mathematics at Michigan State University. His early research was on the use of concrete materials in supporting student learning and led to the development of teaching materials for laboratory environments. Later he helped develop a teaching model to support student experimentation with mathematics.

Susan N. Friel is a Professor of Mathematics Education in the School of Education at the University of North Carolina at Chapel Hill. Her research interests focus on statistics education for middle-grade students and, more broadly, on teachers' professional development and growth in teaching mathematics K–8.

Elizabeth Difanis Phillips is a Senior Academic Specialist in the Mathematics Department of Michigan State University. She is interested in teaching and learning mathematics for both teachers and students. These interests have led to curriculum and professional development projects at the middle school and high school levels, as well as projects related to the teaching and learning of algebra across the grades.

CMP2 Development Staff

Field Test Sites for CMP2

During the development of the revised edition of *Connected Mathematics* (CMP2), more than 100 classroom teachers have field-tested materials at 49 school sites in 12 states and the District of Columbia. This classroom testing occurred over three academic years (2001 through 2004), allowing careful study of the effectiveness of each of the 24 units that comprise the program. A special thanks to the students and teachers at these pilot schools.

Arkansas

Magnolia Public Schools
Kittena Bell*, Judith Trowell*; *Central Elementary School:* Maxine Broom, Betty Eddy, Tiffany Fallin, Bonnie Flurry, Carolyn Monk, Elizabeth Tye; *Magnolia Junior High School:* Monique Bryan, Ginger Cook, David Graham, Shelby Lamkin

Colorado

Boulder Public Schools
Nevin Platt Middle School: Judith Koenig

St. Vrain Valley School District, Longmont
Westview Middle School: Colleen Beyer, Kitty Canupp, Ellie Decker*, Peggy McCarthy, Tanya deNobrega, Cindy Payne, Ericka Pilon, Andrew Roberts

District of Columbia
Capitol Hill Day School: Ann Lawrence

Georgia
University of Georgia, Athens
Brad Findell

Madison Public Schools
Morgan County Middle School: Renee Burgdorf, Lynn Harris, Nancy Kurtz, Carolyn Stewart

Maine
Falmouth Public Schools
Falmouth Middle School: Donna Erikson, Joyce Hebert, Paula Hodgkins, Rick Hogan, David Legere, Cynthia Martin, Barbara Stiles, Shawn Towle*

Michigan

Portland Public Schools
Portland Middle School: Mark Braun, Holly DeRosia, Kathy Dole*, Angie Foote, Teri Keusch, Tammi Wardwell

Traverse City Area Public Schools
Bertha Vos Elementary: Kristin Sak; *Central Grade School:* Michelle Clark; Jody Meyers; *Eastern Elementary:* Karrie Tufts; *Interlochen Elementary:* Mary McGee-Cullen; *Long Lake Elementary:* Julie Faulkner*, Charlie Maxbauer, Katherine Sleder; *Norris Elementary:* Hope Slanaker; *Oak Park Elementary:* Jessica Steed; *Traverse Heights Elementary:* Jennifer Wolfert; *Westwoods Elementary:* Nancy Conn; *Old Mission Peninsula School:* Deb Larimer; *Traverse City East Junior High:* Ivanka Berkshire, Ruthanne Kladder, Jan Palkowski, Jane Peterson, Mary Beth Schmitt; *Traverse City West Junior High:* Dan Fouch*, Ray Fouch

Sturgis Public Schools
Sturgis Middle School: Ellen Eisele

Minnesota

Burnsville School District 191
Hidden Valley Elementary: Stephanie Cin, Jane McDevitt

Hopkins School District 270
Alice Smith Elementary: Sandra Cowing, Kathleen Gustafson, Martha Mason, Scott Stillman; *Eisenhower Elementary:* Chad Bellig, Patrick Berger, Nancy Glades, Kye Johnson, Shane Wasserman, Victoria Wilson; *Gatewood Elementary:* Sarah Ham, Julie Kloos, Janine Pung, Larry Wade; *Glen Lake Elementary:* Jacqueline Cramer, Kathy Hering, Cecelia Morris,

Robb Trenda; *Katherine Curren Elementary:* Diane Bancroft, Sue DeWit, John Wilson; *L. H. Tanglen Elementary:* Kevin Athmann, Lisa Becker, Mary LaBelle, Kathy Rezac, Roberta Severson; *Meadowbrook Elementary:* Jan Gauger, Hildy Shank, Jessica Zimmerman; *North Junior High:* Laurel Hahn, Kristin Lee, Jodi Markuson, Bruce Mestemacher, Laurel Miller, Bonnie Rinker, Jeannine Salzer, Sarah Shafer, Cam Stottler; *West Junior High:* Alicia Beebe, Kristie Earl, Nobu Fujii, Pam Georgetti, Susan Gilbert, Regina Nelson Johnson, Debra Lindstrom, Michele Luke*, Jon Sorensen

Minneapolis School District 1
Ann Sullivan K–8 School: Bronwyn Collins; Anne Bartel* (Curriculum and Instruction Office)

Wayzata School District 284
Central Middle School: Sarajane Myers, Dan Nielsen, Tanya Ravnholdt

White Bear Lake School District 624
Central Middle School: Amy Jorgenson, Michelle Reich, Brenda Sammon

New York
New York City Public Schools
IS 89: Yelena Aynbinder, Chi-Man Ng, Nina Rapaport, Joel Spengler, Phyllis Tam*, Brent Wyso; *Wagner Middle School:* Jason Appel, Intissar Fernandez, Yee Gee Get, Richard Goldstein, Irving Marcus, Sue Norton, Bernadita Owens, Jennifer Rehn*, Kevin Yuhas

* indicates a Field Test Site Coordinator

Ohio

Talawanda School District, Oxford
Talawanda Middle School: Teresa Abrams, Larry Brock, Heather Brosey, Julie Churchman, Monna Even, Karen Fitch, Bob George, Amanda Klee, Pat Meade, Sandy Montgomery, Barbara Sherman, Lauren Steidl

Miami University
Jeffrey Wanko*

Springfield Public Schools
Rockway School: Jim Mamer

Pennsylvania
Pittsburgh Public Schools
Kenneth Labuskes, Marianne O'Connor, Mary Lynn Raith*; *Arthur J. Rooney Middle School:* David Hairston, Stamatina Mousetis, Alfredo Zangaro; *Frick International Studies Academy:* Suzanne Berry, Janet Falkowski, Constance Finseth, Romika Hodge, Frank Machi; *Reizenstein Middle School:* Jeff Baldwin, James Brautigam, Lorena Burnett, Glen Cobbett, Michael Jordan, Margaret Lazur, Tamar McPherson, Melissa Munnell, Holly Neely, Ingrid Reed, Dennis Reft

Texas

Austin Independent School District
Bedichek Middle School: Lisa Brown, Jennifer Glasscock, Vicki Massey

El Paso Independent School District
Cordova Middle School: Armando Aguirre, Anneliesa Durkes, Sylvia Guzman, Pat Holguin*, William Holguin, Nancy Nava, Laura Orozco, Michelle Peña, Roberta Rosen, Patsy Smith, Jeremy Wolf

Plano Independent School District
Patt Henry, James Wohlgehagen*; *Frankford Middle School:* Mandy Baker, Cheryl Butsch, Amy Dudley, Betsy Eshelman, Janet Greene, Cort Haynes, Kathy Letchworth, Kay Marshall, Kelly McCants, Amy Reck, Judy Scott, Syndy Snyder, Lisa Wang; *Wilson Middle School:* Darcie Bane, Amanda Bedenko, Whitney Evans, Tonelli Hatley, Sarah (Becky) Higgs, Kelly Johnston, Rebecca McElligott, Kay Neuse, Cheri Slocum, Kelli Straight

Washington

Evergreen School District
Shahala Middle School: Nicole Abrahamsen, Terry Coon*, Carey Doyle, Sheryl Drechsler, George Gemma, Gina Helland, Amy Hilario, Darla Lidyard, Sean McCarthy, Tilly Meyer, Willow Nuewelt, Todd Parsons, Brian Pederson, Stan Posey, Shawn Scott, Craig Sjoberg, Lynette Sundstrom, Charles Switzer, Luke Youngblood

Wisconsin

Beaver Dam Unified School District
Beaver Dam Middle School: Jim Braemer, Jeanne Frick, Jessica Greatens, Barbara Link, Dennis McCormick, Karen Michels, Nancy Nichols*, Nancy Palm, Shelly Stelsel, Susan Wiggins

---

* indicates a Field Test Site Coordinator

Reviews of CMP to Guide Development of CMP2

Before writing for CMP2 began or field tests were conducted, the first edition of *Connected Mathematics* was submitted to the mathematics faculties of school districts from many parts of the country and to 80 individual reviewers for extensive comments.

School District Survey Reviews of CMP

Arizona
Madison School District #38 (Phoenix)

Arkansas
Cabot School District,
Little Rock School District,
Magnolia School District

California
Los Angeles Unified
School District

Colorado
St. Vrain Valley School District
(Longmont)

Florida
Leon County Schools (Tallahassee)

Illinois
School District #21 (Wheeling)

Indiana
Joseph L. Block Junior High
(East Chicago)

Kentucky
Fayette County Public Schools
(Lexington)

Maine
Selection of Schools

Massachusetts
Selection of Schools

Michigan
Sparta Area Schools

Minnesota
Hopkins School District

Texas
Austin Independent School District,
The El Paso Collaborative for
Academic Excellence,
Plano Independent School District

Wisconsin
Platteville Middle School

Individual Reviewers of CMP

Arkansas
Deborah Cramer; Robby Frizzell *(Taylor)*; Lowell Lynde *(University of Arkansas, Monticello)*; Leigh Manzer *(Norfork)*; Lynne Roberts *(Emerson High School, Emerson)*; Tony Timms *(Cabot Public Schools)*; Judith Trowell *(Arkansas Department of Higher Education)*

California
José Alcantar *(Gilroy)*; Eugenie Belcher *(Gilroy)*; Marian Pasternack *(Lowman M. S. T. Center, North Hollywood)*; Susana Pezoa *(San Jose)*; Todd Rabusin *(Hollister)*; Margaret Siegfried *(Ocala Middle School, San Jose)*; Polly Underwood *(Ocala Middle School, San Jose)*

Colorado
Janeane Golliher *(St. Vrain Valley School District, Longmont)*; Judith Koenig *(Nevin Platt Middle School, Boulder)*

Florida
Paige Loggins *(Swift Creek Middle School, Tallahassee)*

Illinois
Jan Robinson *(School District #21, Wheeling)*

Indiana
Frances Jackson *(Joseph L. Block Junior High, East Chicago)*

Kentucky
Natalee Feese *(Fayette County Public Schools, Lexington)*

Maine
Betsy Berry *(Maine Math & Science Alliance, Augusta)*

Maryland
Joseph Gagnon *(University of Maryland, College Park)*; Paula Maccini *(University of Maryland, College Park)*

Massachusetts
George Cobb *(Mt. Holyoke College, South Hadley)*; Cliff Kanold *(University of Massachusetts, Amherst)*

Michigan
Mary Bouck *(Farwell Area Schools)*; Carol Dorer *(Slauson Middle School, Ann Arbor)*; Carrie Heaney *(Forsythe Middle School, Ann Arbor)*; Ellen Hopkins *(Clague Middle School, Ann Arbor)*; Teri Keusch *(Portland Middle School, Portland)*; Valerie Mills *(Oakland Schools, Waterford)*; Mary Beth Schmitt *(Traverse City East Junior High, Traverse City)*; Jack Smith *(Michigan State University, East Lansing)*; Rebecca Spencer *(Sparta Middle School, Sparta)*; Ann Marie Nicoll Turner *(Tappan Middle School, Ann Arbor)*; Scott Turner *(Scarlett Middle School, Ann Arbor)*

Minnesota
Margarita Alvarez *(Olson Middle School, Minneapolis)*; Jane Amundson *(Nicollet Junior High, Burnsville)*; Anne Bartel *(Minneapolis Public Schools)*; Gwen Ranzau Campbell *(Sunrise Park Middle School, White Bear Lake)*; Stephanie Cin *(Hidden Valley Elementary, Burnsville)*; Joan Garfield *(University of Minnesota, Minneapolis)*; Gretchen Hall *(Richfield Middle School, Richfield)*; Jennifer Larson *(Olson Middle School, Minneapolis)*; Michele Luke *(West Junior High, Minnetonka)*; Jeni Meyer *(Richfield Junior High, Richfield)*; Judy Pfingsten *(Inver Grove Heights Middle School, Inver Grove Heights)*; Sarah Shafer *(North Junior High, Minnetonka)*; Genni Steele *(Central Middle School, White Bear Lake)*; Victoria Wilson *(Eisenhower Elementary, Hopkins)*; Paul Zorn *(St. Olaf College, Northfield)*

New York
Debra Altenau-Bartolino *(Greenwich Village Middle School, New York)*; Doug Clements *(University of Buffalo)*; Francis Curcio *(New York University, New York)*; Christine Dorosh *(Clinton School for Writers, Brooklyn)*; Jennifer Rehn *(East Side Middle School, New York)*; Phyllis Tam *(IS 89 Lab School, New York)*;

Marie Turini *(Louis Armstrong Middle School, New York)*; Lucy West *(Community School District 2, New York)*; Monica Witt *(Simon Baruch Intermediate School 104, New York)*

Pennsylvania
Robert Aglietti *(Pittsburgh)*; Sharon Mihalich *(Freeport)*; Jennifer Plumb *(South Hills Middle School, Pittsburgh)*; Mary Lynn Raith *(Pittsburgh Public Schools)*

Texas
Michelle Bittick *(Austin Independent School District)*; Margaret Cregg *(Plano Independent School District)*; Sheila Cunningham *(Klein Independent School District)*; Judy Hill *(Austin Independent School District)*; Patricia Holguin *(El Paso Independent School District)*; Bonnie McNemar *(Arlington)*; Kay Neusc *(Plano Independent School District)*; Joyce Polanco *(Austin Independent School District)*; Marge Ramirez *(University of Texas at El Paso)*; Pat Rossman *(Baker Campus, Austin)*; Cindy Schimek *(Houston)*; Cynthia Schneider *(Charles A. Dana Center, University of Texas at Austin)*; Uri Treisman *(Charles A. Dana Center, University of Texas at Austin)*; Jacqueline Weilmucnster *(Grapevine-Colleyville Independent School District)*; LuAnn Weynand *(San Antonio)*; Carmen Whitman *(Austin Independent School District)*; James Wohlgehagen *(Plano Independent School District)*

Washington
Ramesh Gangolli *(University of Washington, Seattle)*

Wisconsin
Susan Lamon *(Marquette University, Hales Corner)*; Steve Reinhart *(retired, Chippewa Falls Middle School, Eau Claire)*

What Do You Expect?
Probability and Expected Value

The Student Edition pages for the Unit Opener follow page 16.

What Do You Expect?
Probability and Expected Value

Goals of the Unit

- Interpret experimental and theoretical probabilities and the relationship between them

- Distinguish between equally likely and non-equally likely outcomes

- Review strategies for identifying possible outcomes and analyzing probabilities, such as using lists or tree diagrams

- Determine if a game is fair or unfair

- Analyze situations that involve two stages (or two actions)

- Use area models to analyze situations that involve two stages

- Determine the expected value of a probability situation

- Analyze situations that involve binomial outcomes

- Use probability and expected value to make decision

Developing Students' Mathematical Habits

The overall goal of *Connected Mathematics* is to help students develop sound mathematical habits. Through their work in this unit, students learn important questions to ask themselves, such as:

- *What are the possible outcomes for the event(s) in this situation?*

- *Are these outcomes equally likely?*

- *Is this a fair or unfair situation?*

- *Can I compute the theoretical probabilities or do I conduct an experiment?*

- *How can I determine the probability of the outcome of one event followed by a second event?*

- *How can I use expected value to help me make decisions?*

Overview

What Do You Expect? is the second probability unit in the *Connected Mathematics* curriculum. The work in this unit assumes that students are familiar with the basic ideas of probability that are presented in the grade 6 unit, *How Likely Is It?* If some or all of your students have not explored the concepts covered in that unit, you will need to prepare them for the mathematics they will encounter in *What Do You Expect?* or consider teaching *How Likely Is It?* If your students have studied *How Likely Is It?*, Investigation 1 of this unit should be a sufficient review, as well as an extension, of the ideas with which they are already acquainted. Through their work in this unit, students will deepen and expand their understanding of basic probability concepts.

Summary of Investigations

Investigation 1
Evaluating Games of Chance

Investigation 1 uses a variety of situations that provide students a chance to review both experimental and theoretical probabilities, equally likely events, fair/unfair games, and strategies for determining theoretical probabilities. Spinners, choosing marbles from two buckets, and rolling two number cubes provide the settings. These situations also introduce two-stage events. For example, students spin a spinner twice and then look at the outcomes of a match/no-match.

Investigation 2
Analyzing Situations Using an Area Model

Investigation 2 uses the area model as a way to analyze the theoretical probability of two-stage events. The two-stage events used are spinning two spinners, choosing paths in a game, and choosing a marble at random from a container chosen at random.

Investigation 3
Expected Value

In Investigation 3, the two-stage event is a one-and-one free-throw situation. A player with a 60% free-throw shooting average goes for a one-and-one. That is, the player shoots the first free throw and then either takes a second free throw (if the first one was made) or does not get a second chance (if the first free throw was missed). After determining experimental probabilities that the player will get a score of 0, 1, or 2, students find the theoretical probability by using an area model. Students determine the long-term average (expected value) for the situation and explore expected value in a variety of different probability settings.

Investigation 4
Binomial Outcomes

Students are introduced to binomial situations by taking a four-item true-false quiz where each answer is determined by tossing a coin. Students then find the expected value (or average score) for guessing. Students also use lists or trees to determine outcomes. The situations lead naturally to Pascal's Triangle, which is explored in the ACE.

Mathematics Background

The following is a summary of the basic ideas that are covered in the grade 6 probability unit, *How Likely Is It?*, and descriptions of the new mathematical ideas students will encounter in *What Do You Expect?*

Basic Probability Concepts

The term *probability* is applied to situations that have uncertain outcomes on individual trials but a predictable pattern of outcomes over many trials. For example, when we toss a fair coin, we are uncertain whether it will come up heads or tails; but we do know that, over the long run, we will get heads about half of the time and tails about half of the time. This does not mean that we can't get several heads in a row. Nor does it mean that if we get a head on one toss, we are more likely to get tails on the next. This concept of uncertainty on an individual outcome but predictable regularity in the long run is often difficult for students. Students need a variety of experiences that challenge their prior conceptions before they grasp this basic concept of probability.

If we toss a tack into the air, we know that it will land either on its head or its side. If we toss a tack many times, we can use the ratio of the number of times it lands on its side to the total number of tosses to estimate the likelihood that the tack will land on its side. Since this ratio is found by experimentation, it is called an *experimental probability*. Many uses of probability in daily life, such as weather forecasts and sports predictions, are based on experimental probabilities.

This unit offers many opportunities for students to collect data through experimentation and to use their data to assign experimental probabilities to the possible outcomes. It is important for students to realize that comparison of samples with small numbers of trials may show wide variation among the samples, and that only through experimentation over many trials can good estimates be made about what will happen in the long run. In other words, experimental probabilities must be based on a great number of trials relative to the number of possible outcomes in order to have reasonable predictability. In some situations, such as tossing a fair coin, we can also find a *theoretical probability*. We know that a fair coin will land either heads up or tails up and that each outcome is *equally likely*. Since each of the two outcomes is equally likely, the probability that a fair coin will land heads up is 1 out of 2, or $\frac{1}{2}$. In a situation where all events are equally likely, the theoretical probability can be expressed as:

$$P\,(\text{outcome}) = \frac{\text{number of possible favorable outcomes}}{\text{total number of possible outcomes}}$$

The theoretical probability of getting a head on one toss of a fair coin is:

$$P(\text{head}) = \frac{\text{number of possible favorable outcomes}}{\text{total number of possible outcomes}} = \frac{1}{2}$$

Another example of a situation for which we can find a theoretical probability is the rolling of a number cube. The six possible outcomes are 1, 2, 3, 4, 5, and 6 and each are equally likely to occur on any single roll. Thus,

$$P(1) = P(2) = P(3) = P(4) = P(5) = P(6) = \frac{1}{6}.$$

We can use this theoretical probability to estimate that if a number cube is rolled many times, we could expect each number to be rolled about $\frac{1}{6}$ of the time.

Probabilities, whether obtained through theoretical analysis or experimentation, are useful for predicting what should happen over the long run. Yet, a probability does not tell us exactly what will happen. If we toss a coin 40 times, we may not get exactly 20 heads; but if we toss a coin 1,000 times, the ratio of heads to the number of tosses is likely to be fairly close to $\frac{1}{2}$. Experimental data gathered over many trials should produce probabilities that are close to the theoretical probabilities; this idea is sometimes called the *Law of Large Numbers* (see discussion of this on page 9). If we can calculate a theoretical probability, we can use it to predict what will happen in the long run rather than having to rely on experimentation alone.

Theoretical Probability Models: Lists and Tree Diagrams

Students who have studied the grade 6 probability unit, *How Likely Is It?,* have already learned quite a bit about conducting simulations to find experimental probabilities and making organized lists of possible outcomes or tree diagrams to find theoretical probabilities. In this unit, they will continue to work with these familiar strategies, while learning a new strategy for finding theoretical probabilities for two-stage events—constructing area models to represent the possible outcomes.

Tree diagrams can be used throughout the unit. They offer students a way to determine all the possible outcomes in a situation systematically, particularly those that are two-stage situations. For example, suppose a spinner divided into three equal sections is spun (stage 1) and a six-sided number cube is rolled (stage 2).

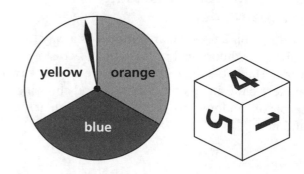

The possible outcomes can be shown in a list and a tree diagram.

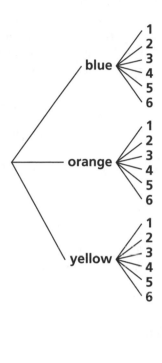

Spinner	Number Cube
blue	1
blue	2
blue	3
blue	4
blue	5
blue	6
orange	1
orange	2
orange	3
orange	4
orange	5
orange	6
yellow	1
yellow	2
yellow	3
yellow	4
yellow	5
yellow	6

In this unit, students use tree diagrams to find the number of equally likely outcomes in situations with a great number of possible outcomes. Tree diagrams are particularly useful for listing outcomes in situations involving a series of actions in which each outcome of a particular action is equally likely. Such situations include rolling a number cube twice, rolling two number cubes, tossing a coin four times, tossing four coins; or choosing several items from a menu, such as a sandwich, a drink, and a dessert. However, when there are many possibilities at a particular stage, tree diagrams can become unwieldy.

Tree diagrams can be used as a basis for understanding the multiplication of probabilities. Multiplication occasions do arise, but building facility with determining such situations is beyond the scope of this unit. Students do not yet understand enough about probability to know when and why it is appropriate to multiply probabilities.

Theoretical Probability Models: Area Models

Area models, like tree diagrams, are useful for finding probabilities in situations involving successive events, such as a basketball player who is allowed to attempt a second free throw only if the first succeeds. Unlike tree diagrams, an area model is particularly powerful in situations in which the possible outcomes are not equally likely.

The following steps demonstrate how to create an area model to show the probability that Nishi, a player with a 60% free-throw average, will score 0, 1, or 2 points in a two-try free-throw situation in basketball. In a two-try situation, the player will get to attempt a second free throw whether or not the first free throw succeeds.

The first try has two possible outcomes, making or missing the basket. The probability of missing the basket is 40% or 0.4 or $\frac{40}{100}$. The probability of making the basket is 60% or 0.6 or $\frac{60}{100}$. The grid below is shaded to indicate this.

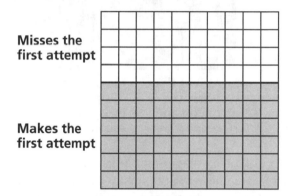

Misses the first attempt

Makes the first attempt

The second try has the same two possible outcomes. These are marked vertically on the grid.

	Makes the second attempt					Misses the second attempt			

Misses the first attempt

Makes the first attempt

The probability that Nishi will make her second try is 60% of the time that she has already made her first try, or 36% of the time. The probability that Nishi will miss her second try is 40% of the time that she makes her first try, or 24% of the time.

If she missed the first try, she still hits the second one 60% of the time. So the probability of getting a score of 0 is $\frac{16}{100}$, getting a score of 1 is $\frac{48}{100}$, and getting a score of 2 is $\frac{36}{100}$. The grid below indicates this, and each region is labeled with the number of points it represents.

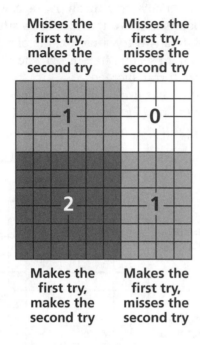

Misses the first try, makes the second try | **Misses the first try, misses the second try**

1 | 0

2 | 1

Makes the first try, makes the second try | **Makes the first try, misses the second try**

To use a tree-diagram approach in a situation where outcomes are not equally likely, each branch of the tree must be weighted by the probability that it will be chosen. This idea is quite difficult for students at this stage to understand; they have used tree diagrams only in situations involving equally likely outcomes. An area analysis makes the weighting more obvious. It is not recommended that you introduce this idea to your students now, but shown here is a tree diagram that works.

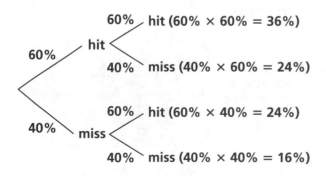

Students, however, will sometimes make a modified version of a weighted tree diagram, pictured below. Such a student might choose a large number of situations (here: 100), then indicate how many of these he would expect to occur on each first branch (here: 60 and 40, corresponding to Nishi's percent of free-throw success). Then each of these numbers is broken down proportionally for the next stage. In effect, this is the same idea as above, but is more accessible to students at this stage of their study of probability.

In Problem 3.1, students explore the probabilities of getting a score of 0, 1, or 2 for a person with a 60% free-throw average in a one-and-one situation.

Consider one more example of these ideas. In Investigation 2, students consider a path game (below) in which a player chooses a path at random at each intersection. Students are to figure out the probability of landing in either Cave A or Cave B. Note: The diagram and the analysis here show a different way of labeling the analysis than in the Investigation. This gives you an alternative strategy in case your students are struggling.

The area model for this game is first split into thirds to indicate the three equally likely paths at the first intersection: the upper path, the middle path, and the lower path. Then each of these thirds is split according to the later intersections (if any), resulting in the model on the following page.

Upper path	path 1	path 2
Middle path	path 3	
Lower path	path 4	path 5	path 6

From the area model, it is clear that the 6 paths are not equally likely. Path 3, for instance, has a probability of $\frac{1}{3}$, while path 4 has probability of $\frac{1}{9}$.

A simple tree diagram would not show this:

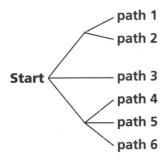

But the modified tree diagram described below would in fact represent the differences in the probabilities for each path. Path 3 occurs 12 out of the 36 games, more than any of the other paths.

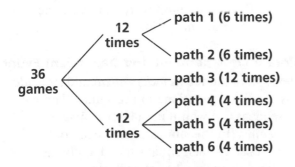

Compound Events and Multi-Stage Events

If you are interested in the probability of an event, A, happening, and there are several ways that A can happen, then A is a *compound event*. The probability of A happening is the sum of the probabilities of each possible way that A can happen. For example, if you toss two coins and are interested in finding the probability that you will get a match, there are two ways that A can happen. You can get two heads or two tails. The probability of A, $P(A)$, is the sum of the probabilities

of each outcome where two coins match.
$P(A) = P(t, t) + P(h, h) = \frac{1}{4} + \frac{1}{4} = \frac{1}{2}$.

An event is a *multi-stage event* if it takes more than one action to create an outcome. In the example above, event A is a two-stage event, since it takes the toss of two coins (or one coin, twice) to get an outcome. The possibilities are (t, t), (t, h), (h, t), and (h, h). The question is, what is the probability of each of these outcomes? If the coin is fair, then each coin toss has a probability of landing tails or heads. The coin tosses are *independent* of each other. How the coin lands on a given toss is not affected by any previous toss. Here $P(t, t) = P(t) \times P(t)$ or $\frac{1}{2} \times \frac{1}{2} = \frac{1}{4}$. The same is true for each of the four possible outcomes.

For a player with a 60% free-throw average in a one-and-one situation, whether or not the player gets to take a second try depends on the result of the first try. Here the second try is *dependent* on the result of the first attempt. Thus, $P(0 \text{ points})$ can only be achieved in one way and that is to miss the first try. The probability of a miss on the first try is 0.4. Thus, $P(0 \text{ points}) = 0.4$. There are two possible outcomes resulting from a hit on the first try; the player can hit or miss the second try. So we have $P(1 \text{ point}) = P(h, h) = 0.6 \times 0.6 = 0.36$ and $P(h, m) = P(1 \text{ point}) = 0.6 \times 0.4 = 0.24$. In a one-and-one free-throw situation, we have three possible outcomes, one of which is a one-stage event (0 points) and two of which are two-stage events (1 point or 2 points). The deciding factor is that the second action is dependent on the result of the first action. The sum of all possible outcomes is $P(0 \text{ points}) + P(1 \text{ point}) + P(2 \text{ points}) = 0.4 + 0.24 + 0.36 = 1$.

Expected Value

The "in the long run" perspective of probability is key to understanding probability. Rather than *guarantee* what will happen on a particular trial or even in the short run, probability models *predict* what will happen in the long run over many trials. Often, this is the most valuable information we can gain about a probability situation: a prediction of the expected value of the situation. The *expected value* is the average of the payoff of each outcome weighted by its probability. It predicts long-run expectations.

In this unit, students are introduced to expected value in an informal yet concrete way. We do not expect them to develop a formal definition of expected value or to use a formula for finding it. In fact, students might never use the term expected value in their work in this unit, instead thinking of the concept as "what is expected in the long run." However, expected value is vocabulary that the student text uses frequently once it is introduced.

Expected value goes beyond basic probabilities. It uses value, such as points earned in a game or money won in a contest, to weight each possible outcome by then computing the average points or dollars we can expect per game or contest in the long run. You can think of expected value as a "weighted average."

Example 1

Consider the long-term average or expected value for a player with a 60% free-throw average in two-try free-throw situations.

If the player goes to the line 100 times, then he/she expects:

A score of 0 to occur 16 times for a total of 0 points and a score of 1 to occur 48 times for a total of 48 points and a score of 2 to occur 36 times for a total of 72 points.

The total number of points expected in 100 situations is $0 + 48 + 72 = 120$ points. The average number of points expected in 100 trials is 120 points ÷ 100 trials or 1.2 points per trial.

Example 2

We could also arrive at this result by the computation

$\frac{16}{100}(0) + \frac{48}{100}(1) + \frac{36}{100}(2) = \frac{0}{100} + \frac{48}{100} + \frac{72}{100} = 1.2$,

which shows each payoff weighted by the probability that it will occur.

The second example is closer to the mathematical definition of expected value but more conceptually difficult for students and is not directly addressed in this unit. Rather, students compute the expected value in steps, as shown in example 1.

Example 3

The expected value for a player with a 60% free-throw average in a one-and-one situation is:

$\frac{40}{100}(0) + \frac{24}{100}(1) + \frac{36}{100}(2) = \frac{96}{100} = 0.96$

A natural question is what free-throw average for a player gives an expected value of exactly 1 point. This question has a surprising answer. The following is a mathematical analysis that shows

how problems such as this one may be revisited in high school when students are ready to solve quadratic equations.

Let p represent the probability that a player will make the free throw. Then, $(1 - p)$ represents the probability that the player will miss the free throw. Thus, the probability of

- making 0 points is $(1 - p)$
- making 1 point is $p(1 - p)$
- making 2 points is $p \times p$, or p^2

The expected value is thus:

P(2 points) $\times$ 2 + P(1 point) $\times$ 1 + P(0 points) $\times$ 0

Symbolically,

$p^2 \times 2 + p(1 - p) \times 1 + (1 - p) \times 0$

Setting the expected value equal to 1, we can solve for p:

$p^2 \times 2 + p(1 - p) \times 1 + (1 - p) \times 0 = 1$
$2p^2 + p - p^2 + 0 = 1$
$p^2 + p = 1$

Using the quadratic formula to solve the resulting quadratic equation, $p^2 + p - 1 = 0$, yields:

$$p = \frac{-1 + \sqrt{1 + 4}}{2} = \frac{-1 + \sqrt{5}}{2}$$

This is the golden ratio, which is approximately 0.6180339887. The golden ratio is the proportion of length to width of a rectangle that many people consider to be the most beautiful rectangle. Many ancient Greek buildings were built with facades that incorporate this ratio.

More on Independent and Dependent Events

Please note the terms *independent* and *dependent events* are not mentioned in this unit. Naming these ideas can wait until a later course in probability. In this unit, students need only to make sense of each situation and apply the appropriate probability at each stage.

The idea of *independent* and *dependent* events is introduced informally. A more formal approach is often a major focus of probability study in high school and college courses. Yet, we feel it is important to introduce this concept because many students working through a basic probability unit such as this one develop the belief that *all* events are independent.

Suppose you twice choose a marble from a bag containing two red marbles and two blue marbles. If you replace the chosen marble after the first choice, the two choices will be independent of each other, because what you choose the first time will not affect what you choose the second time. If you do not replace the chosen marble, the second choice will be dependent on the first choice, because the probability of choosing each color the second time depends on the color chosen on the first choice. For example, if you choose a red marble the first time and do not replace it, the probability of chosing a red marble the second time is $\frac{1}{3}$ rather than $\frac{1}{2}$. Yet if you had chosen a blue marble the first time, the probability of choosing red the second time would be $\frac{2}{3}$. It is in this sense that the probability of choosing a red on the second choice is a dependent probability.

In this unit, students analyze dependent events by using the situation to help make sense of the sequence of actions. They look at the context and determine the sequence of actions and the possibilities at each step in the sequence. The steps in the sequence guide the apportioning of the total area in an area model, or the designing of a tree diagram representing all possible outcomes. Then, each portion of area in an area model, or each path on a tree diagram, is compared to the total area or the total number of possible outcomes to form probability statements.

Consider an area model for the marbles without replacement:

Second Choice
(with red removed)

		B	B	R
First Choice	B	BB	BB	BR
	B	BB	BB	BR
	R	RB	RB	RR
	R	RB	RB	RR

The probability of choosing two reds is $\frac{1}{6}$. Note that the probability of choosing a red on the second choice is greater if blue was chosen on the first choice.

As students use an area model to make sense of two-stage probability situations, take any opportunity to help those who seem ready to see the connection to multiplying probabilities. For example, in the preceding 60% two free-throw situation,

$$P(\text{score of } 0) = \frac{40}{100} \times \frac{40}{100} = \frac{16}{100}$$

$$P(\text{score of } 1) = \frac{60}{100} \times \frac{40}{100} + \frac{40}{100} \times \frac{60}{100} = \frac{48}{100}$$

$$P(\text{score of } 2) = \frac{60}{100} \times \frac{60}{100} = \frac{36}{100}$$

As an area model is also used to develop an understanding of the multiplication of fractions, many students will see this connection naturally.

The Law of Large Numbers

The Law of Large Numbers tells us that as we conduct more and more trials, the probabilities drawn from the experimental data should grow closer to the actual probabilities. This idea is difficult for students to grasp; they need time to experiment to develop an understanding of this concept. As you work with the class, talk about the need for many trials in conducting an experiment to find experimental probabilities.

Binomial Events and Pascal's Triangle

Many interesting probability situations are of the type where there are exactly two equally likely possible outcomes: yes or no, boy or girl, true or false, heads or tails, etc. These are called binomial events. If students guess at every answer for a five-item true/false quiz, there are 32 ways to answer the quiz, but only one of them has all five answers correct. The probability of getting all five answers correct is $\frac{1}{32}$. A similar situation involves the families in the town of Ortonville. Each family has exactly five children and they all agree to name their children the same names. There are 32 ways to arrange five children according to numbers of boys and girls (BBGGG, BGBGG, GGGGG, etc.) The probability of a family having exactly five girls is $\frac{1}{32}$.

The probability of having two boys and three girls is $\frac{10}{32}$. Once one binomial situation has been analyzed it is easy to analyze another binomial situation.

Pascal's Triangle is used to analyze binomial probabilities. The triangle of numbers is named after the seventeenth century mathematician Blaise Pascal. However, the array was in existence long before this. The first five rows are below:

Pascal's Triangle

```
    1  1
   1  2  1
  1  3  3  1
 1  4  6  4  1
1  5  10  10  5  1
```

Pascal's Triangle and a Coin Toss

Row	Number of Outcomes
1	Tossing 1 coin
2	Tossing 2 coins
3	Tossing 3 coins
4	Tossing 4 coins
5	Tossing 5 coins

Pascal's Triangle and a True/False Test

Row	Number of Outcomes
1	True/false test with 1 question
2	True/false test with 2 questions
3	True/false test with 3 questions
4	True/false test with 4 questions
5	True/false test with 5 questions

The first row states that there are two possible outcomes for tossing a coin, a head or a tail, and there are two possible outcomes for answering a true/false question, true or false. The fifth row states that there is 1 way to get five heads, (1 way to answer all questions true), 5 ways to get four heads and one tail (5 ways to answer four questions true and one question false), 10 ways to get three heads and two tails (10 ways to answer three questions true and two question false), 10 ways to get two heads and three tails (10 ways to answer two questions true and three question false), 5 ways to get one head and four tails (5 ways to answer one questions true and four question false), and 1 way to get five tails (1 way to answer all questions false). A similar analysis can be used for any other binomial situation.

Pascal's Triangle is only presented in an ACE, but students recognize the similarity between the binomial situations and can use previous results to analyze a new situation. An example is a problem that involves a Baseball Series between the evenly matched Gazelles (G) and Bobcats (B). The Gazelles have won the first two games. What is the probability that the series will end in four games? Five games? Six games? Seven games? To answer these questions students analyze the possible outcomes of the last five games. Again there are 32 outcomes. The probability of ending in 4, 5, 6, or 7 games equals $(\frac{1}{4})$. However, the Gazelles have a greater chance of winning the series.

Content Connections to Other Units

Big Idea	Prior Work	Future Work
Gathering data	Gathering, analyzing, and displaying data to show trends (*Data About Us*)	Understanding and describing data distributions, sampling techniques, and using samples to predict population behaviors (*Data Distributions, Samples and Populations*)
Understanding probability	Understanding chance as the likelihood of a particular event occurring; studying equally likely outcomes and randomness (*How Likely Is It?*)	Using probabilities to make inferences and predictions about populations based on analysis of population samples (*Data Distributions, Samples and Populations*)
Understanding, determining, and reasoning with experimental probabilities	Conducting trials of a game or experiment to determine experimental probabilities (*How Likely Is It?*); organizing data collected from experiments (*Variables and Patterns; Moving Straight Ahead*)	Using data collected from samples of populations to determine experimental probabilities; developing techniques for simulating situations in order to collect and organize data (*Data Distributions, Samples and Populations*)
Understanding, determining, and reasoning with theoretical probability	Analyzing simple games to determine theoretical probabilities (*How Likely Is It?*); using an area model for understanding addition and multiplication of fractions (*Bits and Pieces II*)	Developing strategies for analyzing complex games or situations to determine theoretical probabilities (*Data Distributions, Samples and Populations*); developing counting strategies to calculate theoretical probabilities (*Clever Counting* © 2004)
Finding and reasoning with expected value	Studying favorable outcomes, equally likely outcomes, and random outcomes (*How Likely Is It?*)	Using expected values of favorable and unfavorable outcomes to make inferences and predictions; using expected values to make recommendations or to develop solutions to real-world problems (*Data Distributions, Samples and Populations; Clever Counting* © 2004)

Planning for the Unit

Pacing Suggestions and Materials

Investigations and Assessments	Pacing 45–50 min. classes	Materials for Students	Materials for Teachers
1 Evaluating Games of Chance	$4\frac{1}{2}$ days	Labsheets 1.1 and 1.3, bobby pins or paper clips, opaque containers, colored marbles or blocks, number cubes	Transparency 1.1
Mathematical Reflections	$\frac{1}{2}$ day		
Assessment: Check Up 1	$\frac{1}{2}$ day		
2 Analyzing Situations Using an Area Model	$3\frac{1}{2}$ days	Labsheet 2.1, bobby pins or paper clips, number cubes, colored blocks, coins, large sheets of paper and markers, blocks or marbles	Transparencies 2.1–2.3
Mathematical Reflections	$\frac{1}{2}$ day		
Assessment: Partner Quiz	$\frac{1}{2}$ day		
3 Expected Value	$4\frac{1}{2}$ days	Hundredths grids, Labsheets 3.1 and 3.2, bobby pins or paper clips, colored blocks, ten-sided number cubes, large sheets of paper and markers	Transparencies 3.1 and 3.2, transparency of Labsheet 3.2 (optional)
Mathematical Reflections	$\frac{1}{2}$ day		
Assessment: Check Up 2	1 day		
4 Binomial Outcomes	$3\frac{1}{2}$ days	Pennies	Transparency 4.2
Mathematical Reflections	$\frac{1}{2}$ day		
Unit Project	1 day		
Looking Back and Looking Ahead	$\frac{1}{2}$ day		
Assessment: Self Assessment	Take Home		
Assessment: Unit Test	1 day		

Total Time $22\frac{1}{2}$ days

For detailed pacing for Problems within each Investigation, see the Suggested Pacing at the beginning of each investigation.

For pacing with block scheduling, see next page.

Materials for Use in All Investigations	
Calculators, blank transparencies and transparency markers (optional), student notebooks	Blank transparencies and transparency markers (optional)

Pacing for Block Scheduling (90-minute class periods)

Investigation	Suggested Pacing	Investigation	Suggested Pacing
Investigation 1	**2 days**	**Investigation 3**	**$2\frac{1}{2}$ days**
Problem 1.1	$\frac{1}{2}$ day	Problem 3.1	$\frac{1}{2}$ day
Problem 1.2	$\frac{1}{2}$ day	Problem 3.2	$\frac{1}{2}$ day
Problem 1.3	$\frac{1}{2}$ day	Problem 3.3	1 day
Math Reflections	$\frac{1}{2}$ day	Math Reflections	$\frac{1}{2}$ day
Investigation 2	**2 days**	**Investigation 4**	**2 days**
Problem 2.1	$\frac{1}{2}$ day	Problem 4.1	$\frac{1}{2}$ day
Problem 2.2	$\frac{1}{2}$ day	Problem 4.2	$\frac{1}{2}$ day
Problem 2.3	$\frac{1}{2}$ day	Problem 4.3	$\frac{1}{2}$ day
Math Reflections	$\frac{1}{2}$ day	Math Reflections	$\frac{1}{2}$ day

Vocabulary

Essential Terms Developed in This Unit	Useful Terms Referenced in This Unit	Terms Developed in Previous Units
area model	payoff	equally likely
tree diagram	Law of Large Numbers	experimental probability
expected value	sample space	fair game
binomial probability		outcome
		probability
		random
		theoretical probability

Go Online
PHSchool.com
For: Teacher Resources
Web Code: ank-5500

Components

Use the chart below to quickly see which components are available for each Investigation.

Investigation	Labsheets	Additional Practice	Transparencies		Formal Assessment		Assessment Options	
			Problem	Summary	Check Up	Partner Quiz	Multiple-Choice	Question Bank
1	1.1, 1.3	✔	1.1		✔		✔	✔
2	2.1	✔	2.1–2.3			✔	✔	
3	3.1, 3.2	✔	3.1, 3.2				✔	✔
4		✔	4.2		✔			✔
For the Unit		*ExamView* CD-ROM, Web site	LBLA		Unit Test, Notebook Check, Self Assessment		Multiple-Choice, Question Bank, *ExamView* CD-ROM	

Also Available for Use With This Unit

- Parent Guide: take-home letter for the unit
- Implementing CMP
- Spanish Assessment Resources
- Additional online and technology resources

Technology

The Use of Calculators

Connected Mathematics was developed with the belief that calculators should be available and that students should learn when their use is appropriate. For this reason, we do not designate specific problems as "calculator problems." However, in this unit, we suggest that students refrain from using calculators, unless it is specifically noted to use them, so that they are able to understand probability. Rushing to use the calculator does not promote a deep analysis of probability as a ratio, how to compute probabilities, and what an answer means. Converting a ratio to a decimal is helpful for comparing probabilities.

Investigation 2: In the ACE problems for Investigation 2, there is reference to a game called Treasure Hunt. A simple computer version of this game is available at www.math.msu.edu/cmp/Resources/Software.htm

Student Activity CD-ROM

Includes interactive activities to enhance the learning in the Problems within Investigations.

PHSchool.com

For Students Multiple-choice practice with instant feedback, updated data sources, data sets for Tinkerplots data software.

For Teachers Professional development, curriculum support, downloadable forms, and more.

See also www.math.msu.edu/cmp for more resources for both teachers and students.

ExamView® Test Generator

Create multiple versions of practice sheets and tests for course objectives and standardized tests. Includes dynamic questions, online testing, student reports, and all test and practice items in Spanish. Also includes all items in the *Assessment Resources* and *Additional Practice*.

Teacher Express™ CD-ROM

Includes a lesson-planning tool, the Teacher's Guide pages, and all the teaching resources.

LessonLab Online Courses

LessonLab offers comprehensive, facilitated professional development designed to help teachers implement CMP2 and improve student achievement. To learn more, please visit PHSchool.com/cmp2.

Assessment Summary

Ongoing Informal Assessment

Embedded in the Unit

Problems Use students' work from the Problems to check student understanding.

ACE exercises Use ACE exercises for homework assignments to assess student understanding.

Mathematical Reflections Have students summarize their learning at the end of each Investigation.

Looking Back and Looking Ahead At the end of the unit, use the first two sections to allow students to show what they know about the unit.

Additional Resources

Teacher's Guide Use the Check for Understanding feature of some Summaries and the probing questions that appear in the *Launch, Explore,* or *Summarize* sections of all Investigations to check student understanding.

Self Assessment

Notebook Check Students use this tool to organize and check their notebooks before giving them to their teacher. Located in *Assessment Resources*.

Self Assessment At the end of the unit, students reflect on and provide examples of what they learned. Located in *Assessment Resources*.

Formal Assessment

Choose the assessment materials that are appropriate for your students.

Assessment	For Use After	Focus	Student Work
Check Up 1	Invest. 1	Skills	Individual
Partner Quiz	Invest. 2	Rich problems	Pair
Check Up 2	Invest. 3	Skills	Individual
Unit Test	The Unit	Skills, rich problems	Individual
Unit Project	The Unit	Rich problems	Individual or Group

Additional Resources

Multiple-Choice Items Use these items for homework, review, a quiz, or add them to the Unit Test.

Question Bank Choose from these questions for homework, review, or replacements for Quiz, Check Up, or Unit Test questions.

Additional Practice Choose practice exercises for each investigation for homework, review, or formal assessments.

ExamView **CD-ROM** Create practice sheets, review quizzes, and tests with this dynamic software. Give online tests and receive student progress reports. *(All test items are also available in Spanish.)*

Spanish Assessment Resources

Includes Partner Quizzes, Check Ups, Unit Test, Multiple-Choice Items, Question Bank, Notebook Check, and Self-Assessment. Plus, the *ExamView* CD-ROM has all test items in Spanish.

Correlation to Standardized Tests

Investigation	NAEP	Terra Nova CAT6	Terra Nova CTBS	ITBS	SAT10	Local Test
1 Evaluating Games of Chance	D4a, D4c, D4d	✔	✔		✔	
2 Analyzing Situations Using an Area Model	D4e, D4f		✔		✔	
3 Expected Value	D4d, D4h		✔		✔	
4 Binomial Outcomes	D4c, D4f		✔		✔	

NAEP National Assessment of Educational Progress
CAT6/Terra Nova California Achievement Test, 6th Ed.
CTBS/Terra Nova Comprehensive Test of Basic Skills
ITBS Iowa Test of Basic Skills, Form M
SAT10 Stanford Achievement Test, 10th Ed.

Introducing Your Students to *What Do You Expect?*

Many examples of probability and expected value can be found in newspapers and magazines. You could use an example to launch the unit. Then as students progress through this unit, you might encourage them to bring any examples they find to school to share with the class. Another project you might conduct during this unit is to have students investigate whether their state (or a neighboring state) has a lottery and to find out as much as they can about the cost of playing, the probabilities of winning, the payoffs, and the expected values. Note that the expected value for a player of any lottery or casino game is negative.

Using the Unit Opener

Briefly discuss the questions posed at the beginning of the unit. The questions will be answered within the unit, so students are not expected to be able to solve them here. The questions serve as an advanced organizer for what the students will encounter and learn to do during the unit. Take a few minutes to allow ideas from the students with the goal of generating enthusiasm for the kinds of situations in the unit. This can also give you an informal assessment of where your students are on understanding the meaning of probability and expected value.

Using the Mathematical Highlights

The Mathematical Highlights page in the Student Edition provides information to students, parents, and other family members. It gives students a preview of the mathematics and some of the overarching questions that they should ask themselves while studying *What Do You Expect?*

As they work through the unit, students can refer back to the Mathematical Highlights page to review what they have learned and to preview what is still to come. This page also tells students' families what mathematical ideas and activities will be covered as the class works through *What Do You Expect?*

Using the Unit Project

The unit project offers an opportunity for students to apply the probability concepts they have studied, including expected value, in a real-world context. Students are asked to design a new game for a school carnival or to redesign one of the games that was studied in this unit.

The project works well with groups of three or four. This project may be launched near the end of the unit, sometime after Investigation 3. The project will require several hours to complete, though most of this work can be done outside of class. You may want to take half a class period to get students started. Have them form groups, review the project instructions, and then brainstorm their game design. For the next few days, you might reserve the last ten minutes of class for groups to meet, report to each other, get advice from others in class or from you, and do whatever else they need to do to make progress on their projects.

See the Guide to the Unit Project section on page 96 for more information about assigning and assessing the project. There you will find a rubric and samples of student projects. Each sample is followed by a teacher's comments about assessing the project.

Connected Mathematics 2™

What Do You Expect?

Probability and Expected Value

Glenda Lappan

James T. Fey

William M. Fitzgerald

Susan N. Friel

Elizabeth Difanis Phillips

PEARSON

Boston, Massachusetts · Glenview, Illinois · Shoreview, Minnesota · Upper Saddle River, New Jersey

Notes

What Do You Expect?

Probability and Expected Value

 In Raymundo's *Prime Number Multiplication Game*, a player rolls two number cubes. Player A gets 10 points if the product is prime. Player B gets 1 point if the product is not prime. Is Raymundo's game a fair game?

In the district finals, Nishi has just been fouled. She gets to try one free throw. If she makes it, she gets to try a second free throw. Nishi's free-throw average is 60%. Is Nishi most likely to score 0, 1, or 2 points?

 Have you ever had to guess at the answers on a quiz? If you take a four-question true/false quiz and guess on every question, what are your chances of getting every question right?

2   What Do You Expect?

Notes _____

_____

_____

_____

Probabilities can help you make decisions. If there is a 75% chance of rain, you might decide to carry an umbrella. If a baseball player has a .245 batting average, you expect that he is more likely not to get a hit than to get a hit on a given at-bat.

Probabilities can also help you to predict what will happen over the long run. Suppose you and a friend toss a coin before each bus ride to decide who will sit by the window. You can predict that, over the long run, you will sit by the window about half of the time.

Many probability situations involve a payoff—points scored in a game, lives saved by promoting good health, or profit earned from a business venture. You can sometimes find the long-term average payoff called the expected value. For example, when deciding whether to make an investment, a company might figure out how much it can expect to earn over the long run.

In this unit, you will look at questions involving probability and expected value, including the three questions on the opposite page.

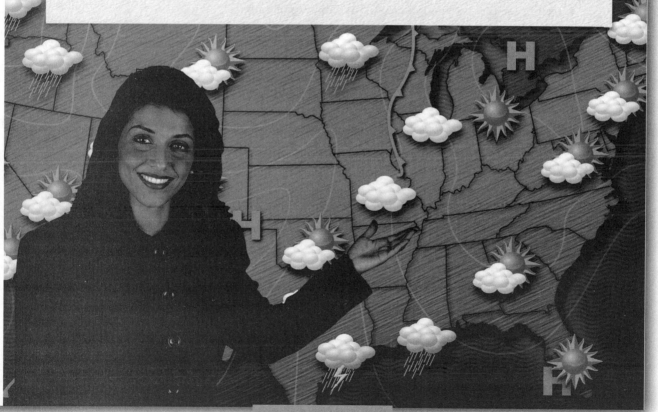

Notes _____

_____

_____

_____

Mathematical Highlights

Probability and Expected Value

In *What Do You Expect?*, you will deepen your understanding of basic probability concepts. You will learn about the expected value of situations involving chance.

You will learn how to

- Interpret experimental and theoretical probabilities and the relationship between them
- Distinguish between equally likely and non-equally likely events
- Review strategies for identifying possible outcomes and analyzing probabilities, such as using lists or tree diagrams
- Determine if a game is fair or unfair
- Analyze situations that involve two stages (or actions)
- Use area models to analyze situations that involve two stages
- Determine the expected value of a probability situation
- Analyze situations that involve binomial outcomes
- Use probability and expected value to make decisions

As you work on problems in this unit, ask yourself questions about situations that involve analyzing probabilities:

What are the possible outcomes for the event(s) in this situation?

Are these outcomes equally likely?

Is this a fair or unfair situation?

Can I compute the theoretical probabilities or do I conduct an experiment?

How can I determine the probability of the outcome of one event followed by a second event?

How can I use expected value to help me make decisions?

4 What Do You Expect?

Notes _____

_____

_____

_____

Investigation 1 — Evaluating Games of Chance

Mathematical and Problem-Solving Goals

- Review basic probability concepts, such as fair game, experimental probability, theoretical probability, and fraction notation for expressing probabilities

- Include a payoff in consideration of the fairness of a game

- Use probability and payoff to calculate the long-term average result of a game of chance

Investigation 1 uses a variety of situations that provide students a chance to review both experimental and theoretical probabilities, equally likely events, fair/unfair games, and strategies for determining theoretical probabilities. Spinners, choosing marbles from two buckets, and rolling two number cubes provide the settings. These situations also introduce two-stage events.

Summary of Problems

Problem 1.1 Matching Colors

Students spin a spinner twice and look at the outcomes of a match/no-match, assigning points for each outcome. Students determine whether the game is fair.

Problem 1.2 Red and Blue Is a Winner!

Students choose one colored marble from each of two buckets. If a blue and a red are chosen, the contestant wins. Students consider the long-term average result of the game.

Problem 1.3 Playing the Multiplication Game

Students roll two number cubes and determine the product of the two numbers. Player A wins if the product is odd, and Player B wins if the product is even. Students must decide if this is a fair game and how many points each player can expect after 36 plays, 100 plays, etc.

	Suggested Pacing	Materials for Students	Materials for Teachers	ACE Assignments
All	5 days		Transparency 1.1 (optional) and Transparency markers	
1.1	$1\frac{1}{2}$ days	Labsheet 1.1 (1 per pair); bobby pins or paper clips (for spinners, 1 per pair)	Transparency 1.1 (optional)	1, 2, 14–19
1.2	$1\frac{1}{2}$ days	Opaque containers (2 per pair or group); colored marbles or blocks (1 blue, 2 yellow, 1 green, and 2 red per pair)		3–10, 20–22, 29
1.3	$1\frac{1}{2}$ days	Labsheet 1.3 (1 per pair); number cubes (2 per pair)		11–13, 23–28, 30–33
MR	$\frac{1}{2}$ day			

1.1 Matching Colors

Goals

- Review basic probability concepts, such as fair game, experimental probability, theoretical probability, and fraction notation for expressing probabilities

- Include a payoff in consideration of the fairness of a game

In this Problem, students spin a spinner twice and then consider the probabilities of the two outcomes: match and no-match. This is an example of a two-stage outcome. Students collect data to determine experimental probabilities and then compare these to the theoretical probabilities.

This problem provides a review of the probability concepts that were developed in *How Likely Is It?* This is also the case with the other two problems in the investigation. In classrooms where students studied that unit in sixth-grade, these problems will go more swiftly than in classrooms where the concepts and vocabulary are new to students.

As a quick introduction, you could do an experiment with tossing pennies to review the definition of probability. Before tossing a coin, ask the class to predict the result.

Suggested Questions Ask questions about the experiment.

- *What is the probability of getting heads?* ($\frac{1}{2}$)

- *What are the outcomes?* (heads and tails)

- *Are they equally likely?* (yes)

Having discussed the theoretical probability of getting heads or tails, toss the coin a few times and record the results. Ask questions using the data.

- *What is the probability of getting a head?* (Answers may vary depending on the results of these tosses, but students should say $\frac{1}{2}$.)

- *What is the probability of getting a tail?*

Tell the class that this is experimental probability. Discuss how the experimental probabilities compare to the theoretical probability. Ask:

- *What would happen if you continue the experiment for more trials?* (The experimental probabilities would get closer to $\frac{1}{2}$.)

Mathematics Background

For background on the Law of Large Numbers, see page 9.

Tell students that they will be analyzing April and Tioko's spinner game to decide whether it is fair.

Suggested Question Ask:

- *What does it mean for a game to be fair?*

Describe the game, and demonstrate how to take one turn (by spinning the spinner twice), using Transparency 1.1. Place the point of a sharpened pencil or a pen through the rounded end of a bobby pin or paper clip and on the center of the spinner. Flick the bobby pin or clip with your finger. Record the results. For example:

Turn Number	Result	Player A's Score	Player B's Score
1	Yellow-blue	0	2

Suggested Questions Ask:

- *Who gets points for this turn? What is the payoff?* (If the two spins land on the same color, Player A scores 1 point. If the spins do not match, Player B scores 2 points.)

Be sure to make clear that Player A scores for a match, regardless of who spins the spinner, and that Player B scores for a no-match, regardless of who spins. This is a common source of student confusion with this game. They may take turns spinning, but a match is always a score for Player A; a no-match for Player B.

- *Is this a fair game? Why or why not?*

Let students offer conjectures, but don't confirm or refute them at this time. This idea will be a focus of the summary of the problem.

Briefly discuss bias with students.

• *You want the results of the spins to be random. You do not want anything about the way you spin the spinners to bias the results. What sorts of things might bias your results?* (slanted desktops, creased paper, always starting with the pointer in the same section, and so on)

Distribute Labsheet 1.1 and a paper clip or bobby pin to each pair of students. Remind the students about making the experiment as random as possible. Have students work in pairs to collect the data, with each partner taking 12 turns.

Explore 1.1

Make sure students are recording data correctly. Once students have found experimental and theoretical probabilities and compared them, have them work on Questions C–D. Help students to see that yellow-blue and blue-yellow are two different outcomes. If students finish early, ask them to find the theoretical probability of making a match if they spin 100 times.

Summarize 1.1

Discuss the students' data and their answers.

Suggested Questions Ask them to explain their reasoning.

• *Is this a fair game? Why or why not?* (The game is not fair; Player B has a big advantage.)

• *Is the game unfair because match and no-match are not equally likely?* (No, the probabilities are equal, but no match gets more points.)

Investigate this question as a class before analyzing the point scheme. Collect some of the individual data from various pairs, and ask students whether the game seems fair based on their individual data. Although 24 is a small number of turns, most pairs' data will probably be fairly close to the theoretical results of 50% match and 50% no-match. Thus, the chance of getting a match versus a no-match is fair, but the awarding of different numbers of points for these two occurrences makes the game unfair.

Combine all the data that the pairs collected. Determine the experimental probability of a match and a no-match based on the entire set of

data by adding the total number of matches and the total number of no-matches. Then, help the class review how to use experimental probabilities to make predictions.

Suggested Questions Ask:

• *Based on the experimental probabilities we found for the class data, do you think Match and No-Match are equally likely?* (yes)

Next, discuss the theoretical probabilities.

• *What are all the possible outcomes of one turn in this game?* (The four possible outcomes are *blue-blue*, blue-yellow, yellow-blue, and yellow-yellow.)

Students may think that blue-yellow and yellow-blue are equivalent. Help them understand that although they both give a no-match, they are different outcomes. There are two ways this could occur.

• *What is the theoretical probability of getting a match?* ($\frac{2}{4}$ or $\frac{1}{2}$)

• *What is the theoretical probability of getting a no-match?* ($\frac{2}{4}$ or $\frac{1}{2}$)

• *How do these theoretical probabilities compare to the experimental probabilities we found from our class data?* (They should be quite close.)

If the class's experimental probabilities differ from the theoretical probabilities, talk about the possible reasons for the discrepancy. The experimental probabilities from the class data are probably closer to the theoretical probabilities than those based on the individual pairs' data.

Now turn to discussion of the point system.

Suggested Questions Ask:

• *If the game were played 100 times, how many points would Player A expect to get?* (Since the probability of a match is $\frac{1}{2}$, player A would expect to win 50 times ($100 \times \frac{1}{2}$) and score 50 points.)

• *How many points would Player B expect to get?* (Player B would expect to win 50 times and score 100 points.)

This is a simple example of the kind of calculation students will do many times in this unit. It may be helpful to notate all of this on the board or projector as a model for future work.

- *Do you think this game is fair? Why or why not? How can you make this a fair game?* (The game is not fair. Each player has the same chance of scoring, but Player B gets twice as many points as Player A for each score. Each player should receive the same number of points per win to make the game fair.)

You can end by taking out a coin and telling the class that you will toss it twice. They win if there are two heads or two tails. You win if there is one of each.

- *Is this a fair game?* (Students should see that this is exactly like the match/no-match in this problem and conclude that the game is fair because there is no point scheme.)

1.1 Matching Colors

Mathematical Goals

- Review basic probability concepts, such as fair game, experimental probability, theoretical probability, and fraction notation for expressing probabilities
- Include a payoff in consideration of the fairness of a game

Launch

- *Who gets points for this turn? What is the payoff?*

Be sure to make clear that Player A scores for a match, regardless of who spins the spinner, and that Player B scores for a no-match, regardless of who spins.

- *Is this a fair game? Why or why not?*

Let students offer conjectures. Briefly discuss bias with students.

- *What sorts of things might bias our results?*

Distribute Labsheet 1.1 and a paper clip or bobby pin to each pair of students. Have students work in pairs to collect the data, with each partner taking 12 turns.

Materials

- Transparency 1.1

Explore

Once students have found experimental and theoretical probabilities and compared them, have them work on Questions C–D.

Materials

- Labsheet 1.1
- Bobby pins or paper clips

Summarize

Discuss the students' data and their answers to the questions. Ask them to explain their reasoning.

- *Is this a fair game? Why or why not?*

Collect some of the individual data from various pairs, and ask students whether the game seems fair based on their individual data. Combine all the data that pairs collected. Determine the experimental probability of a match and a no-match based on the entire set of data by adding the total number of matches and the total number of no-matches. Review how to use experimental probabilities to make predictions.

- *Based on the experimental probabilities we found for the class data, do you think match and no-match are equally likely?*

Discuss the theoretical probabilities.

- *What are all the possible outcomes of one turn in this game?*

- *How do these theoretical probabilities compare to the experimental probabilities we found from our class data?*

Materials

- Student notebooks

Vocabulary

- equally likely
- experimental probability
- outcome
- random
- theoretical probability
- fair game

continued on next page

Talk about the possible reasons for any discrepancy. Discuss the point system.

- _If the game were played 100 times, how many points would Player A expect to get? How many points would Player B expect to get? Do you think this game is fair? Why or why not?_

End by taking out a coin and telling the class that you will toss it twice. They win if there are two heads or two tails. You win if there is one of each. Ask questions about the fairness of this game.

- _Is this a fair game?_

ACE Assignment Guide for Problem 1.1

Differentiated Instruction
Solutions for All Learners

Core 1, 2, 15–18
Other _Connections_ 14, 19

Adapted For suggestions about adapting ACE exercises, see the CMP _Special Needs Handbook_.
Connecting to Prior Units 14: _Bits and Pieces I_

Answers to Problem 1.1

A. Because this is an experiment, answers will vary, but most results will be close to evenly split between match and no-match, resulting in a big win for Player B.

B. 1. blue-blue, blue-yellow, yellow-blue, and yellow-yellow

   2. The theoretical probability of a match is $\frac{2}{4}$ or $\frac{1}{2}$, and the theoretical probability of a no-match is $\frac{2}{4}$ or $\frac{1}{2}$.

   3. The outcomes are equally likely because they have the same chance of being chosen: $\frac{1}{2}$.

C. The experimental probabilities may be close to the theoretical probabilities. However, due to the small number of turns, they may not be exact.

D. The game is not fair. Spinning a match and spinning a no-match are equally likely but the players do not receive the same number of points for each outcome. Scoring one point for a match and one point for a no-match would make it fair.

Red and Blue Is a Winner!

Mathematical Goal

- Use probability and payoff to calculate the long-term average result of a game of chance

In the game in Problem 1.2, contestants choose one colored marble from each of two buckets. If a blue and a red are chosen, the contestant wins. A player pays $1 to play and wins $3 if a red and a blue marble are chosen (in any order). This is a two-stage outcome. Students explore the payoff for the game. That is, after many turns, can the player expect to make money or lose money, and how much?

You could start by reviewing how to use a tree diagram to find all outcomes. The student books show how to use a tree diagram to find the four outcomes in the Match/No-Match game from Problem 1.1. Encourage students to use a list or a tree diagram for the problems that have equally likely outcomes.

Describe the game.

Suggested Questions Demonstrate choosing the two marbles and ask:

- *Is this a winner?*

- *How much money are you ahead or behind at this point?* (If a blue and red occur, then the player is $2 ahead. If not, then the player is $1 behind.)

Optional: Students can play the game 24 times in teams of two to find experimental probabilities, or you could take turns as a whole class, choosing until you have sufficient experimental data.

Let the class explore the problem in pairs.

Explore 1.2

Look for interesting strategies that students use to find the outcomes. Some may use lists; some may use trees.

Students may need help interpreting Question D part (1) and Question E. See summary for a discussion on the use of *or* and *and* in mathematical statements.

Summarize 1.2

Elicit different strategies for finding the outcomes. If you have not done so earlier, this would be a good time to review how to use trees to find outcomes.

Discuss Question D. The probability of a red and a blue marble being chosen is $\frac{1}{12}$. So, in 36 turns, the combination of blue and red occurring is $\frac{1}{12}$ (36) or 3 times. The school would have taken in $36 and paid out $9. So they can expect to be $27 ahead.

Repeat Question D for 96 turns. The blue-red combination would occur $\frac{1}{12}$ (96) or 8 times. So the school takes in $96 and pays out $24. You may want to use the language of *expense* and *income* to connect to students' prior experience with the Grade 7 unit, *Variables and Patterns*.

This game is not a fair game in the sense that the game favors the school. To be fair, both the school and the player would expect to make the same amount. Students might find it interesting to change the rules or payoff to make it a fair game. On the other hand, if the school wants to make money, then the game is a success.

• *What is the probability of getting a red or a blue?*

This question provides an opportunity to explore (review) the use of *or*. In mathematics the word *or* means that one or both of the conditions are true. In everyday English, *or* often means one of the two, but not both. This is different from the mathematical usage. For example, there are eight ways to choose a blue or a red:

Bucket 1	Bucket 2
R	R
R	G
R	Y
B	R
B	G
B	Y
Y	R
G	R

Ask students to think of other probability questions to ask about the data.

1.2 Red and Blue Is a Winner!

Mathematical Goal

- To use probability and payoff to calculate the long-term average result of a game of chance

Launch

Review how to use a tree diagram to find all outcomes. Encourage students to use either strategy for the problems that have equally likely outcomes. Describe the game. Demonstrate choosing the two marbles and ask:

- *Is this a winner?*
- *How much money are you ahead or behind at this point?*

Let the class explore the problem in pairs.

Materials
- tree diagram
- fair game
- payoff

Explore

Look for interesting strategies that students use to find the outcomes. Some may use lists; some may use trees.

Students may need help interpreting Question D part (1) and Question E. See summary for a discussion on the use of *or* and *and* in mathematical statements.

Materials
- Opaque containers
- Colored marbles or blocks

Summarize

Elicit different strategies for finding the outcomes. If you have not done so earlier, this would be a good time to review how to use trees to find outcomes.

Discuss Question D. The probability of a red and a blue marble being chosen is $\frac{1}{12}$. So, in 36 turns, the combination of blue and red occurring is $\frac{1}{12}(36)$ or 3 times. The school would have taken in $36 and paid out $9. So they can expect to be $27 ahead.

Repeat Question D for 96 turns. The blue and red combination would occur $\frac{1}{12}(96)$ or 8 times. So the school takes in $96 and pays out $24.

This game is not a fair game in the sense that the game favors the school. To be fair, both the school and the player would expect to make the same amount. Students might find it interesting to change the rules or payoff to make it a fair game. On the other hand, if the school wants to make money, then the game is a success.

Ask students to think of other probability questions to ask about the data.

Materials
- Student notebooks

ACE Assignment Guide for Problem 1.2

Core 3, 10, 22
Other *Applications* 4–9; *Connections* 20, 21; *Extensions* 29; unassigned choices from previous problems

Adapted For suggestions about adapting Exercise 10 and other ACE exercises, see the CMP *Special Needs Handbook*.

Answers to Problem 1.2

A. Answers will vary. Possible answers: Yes, because there is only one blue marble in Bucket 1 and only one red marble in Bucket 2. Yes, because it is going to be very hard to choose both a red and a blue.

B. Each marble in Bucket 1 is matched to each marble in Bucket 2. There are 12 outcomes: GG, GR, GY, BG, BR, BY, RG, RR, RY, YG, YR, YY.

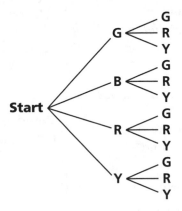

C. Because only one outcome has a blue-red, the probability is $\frac{1}{12}$.

D. 1. The school will collect $36 ($1 per each of the 36 games).

2. The school can expect to pay out $9 ($3 × 3 chances of getting blue-red out of 36 = $9).

3. The school can expect to make about $27.

E. 1. $\frac{1}{12}$

2. $\frac{9}{12} = \frac{3}{4}$

3. $\frac{0}{12}$ or 0

4. $\frac{3}{12} = \frac{1}{4}$

1.3 Playing the Multiplication Game

Mathematical Goal

- Use probability and payoff to calculate the long-term average result of a game of chance

In this game, points are assigned to players based on whether the product of the two numbers rolled on a pair of number cubes is odd or even.

Launch 1.3

You may want to refer to the Roller Derby Game in *How Likely Is It?* In that game students determined the *sum* of two numbers from a pair of number cubes that are rolled. You could play a round of the game with the class.

Suggested Questions Pose a few questions about the probability of obtaining an even sum or an odd sum.

- *What are the possible outcomes (sums)?* (Any number between 2 and 12.)

- *Is each sum equally likely?* (No; 7 is most likely while 2 and 12 are least likely.)

- *How many sums are even?* (six)

- *How many sums are odd?* (five)

- *Do you think odd and even sums are equally likely outcomes?* (In fact they are, because 18 of the 36 outcomes are even and 18 are odd, even though there are only 6 even sums and 5 odd sums.)

Introduce the Multiplication Game, and demonstrate a few rolls. After each roll, ask the class who scored on that roll. If the product of the two numbers shown is odd, Player A scores 1 point. If the product is even, Player B scores 1 point.

Ask students whether they think the game is fair and let them offer their conjectures. Most will probably say it is. The probability of getting an even *sum* is the same as getting an odd sum. It is reasonable to expect the *products* to work the same way. You will return to this question in the summary of the problem.

Remind pairs that when they play the Multiplication Game, they will need to keep track of how many times each product is rolled and whether the product is even or odd.

When you have finished your experiment, you will need to find a way to figure out the theoretical probabilities.

- *When you compare your experimental probabilities to the theoretical probabilities, will they be exactly the same? Why or why not?*

Distribute two number cubes to each pair. Hand out Labsheet 1.3 for students to record their data, or let them find their own method of keeping track of their results.

Explore 1.3

By this time, most students should feel comfortable with experimenting to find experimental probabilities and analyzing a game to find theoretical probabilities. Be on the lookout for students with interesting ways of thinking about how to compute the theoretical probabilities for this game. Some examples follow.

Students often recognize that when one number cube is rolled, the chances of getting an odd or an even number are equal. Some may further reason that because odd × odd = odd, even × even = even, odd × even = even, and even × odd = even, and as these are all equally likely, there are three out of four ways to get an even product. However, some students who reason this way miss reversing the even-odd combination and state the theoretical probability of getting an even product as $\frac{2}{3}$ rather than $\frac{3}{4}$. If this occurs, you will want to be sure to discuss this idea in the summary and have someone explain why $\frac{2}{3}$ is not the correct probability. Note that it would take a large number of trials to decide which is correct from experimental probabilities.

This same question will likely arise with the individual outcomes. That is, students will question whether they should count (2, 1) as different from (1, 2). If students are struggling with this, be sure to spend some time on it in the summary. In this case, the experimental probabilities will probably be convincing. In a large number of trials, the product 2 should occur twice as often as the product 1 because there are these two ways to get 2 with two number cubes, but only one way to get 1 [namely, (1, 1)].

Some students may do a tree diagram. This is possible, but it takes a bit of planning to get the tree diagram (which has 36 branches) on one page.

Some students may just list the 18 different products without considering that some products occur in more than one way. For example, the product 12 occurs with 2×6, 6×2, 3×4, or 4×3.

Some students may use a grid as they did when analyzing sums in the unit *How Likely Is It?*

Summarize 1.3

Begin with Question A, finding the experimental probabilities. You could look at the data from a couple of the groups and then combine the data from all of the groups. Ask the class to compare the experimental probabilities from a small group and then from the entire class. Students should be able to point out that the larger samples give more reliable results.

To look more closely at the results of students' experimentation, you could make a line plot that shows the number of times each product came up as your students played the game. Below is the beginning of a class line plot, with one pair's data displayed (Figure 1).

Once the data from the entire class have been pooled, the class can compute the overall experimental probabilities and use them to predict which products occur most often and whether or not the game is fair. It would be helpful for each pair of students to compare the experimental probabilities from their own data with the experimental probabilities from the class data. The accumulated data should make it clear that odd products occur only about 25% of the time.

Now move to analyzing the theoretical probabilities. Discuss various strategies. Students may have made an organized list, a tree diagram, or a chart to show all the possibilities. If students have different strategies for analyzing the outcomes, it is important to help students see how these strategies are connected.

Suggested Questions Ask:

- *In the tree diagram, how is one roll of the number cubes represented?* (By a branch at the end of the tree.)

- *How is one roll represented in the chart?* (By a section in the chart.)

- *How is one roll represented in the list?* (By an ordered pair.)

Some students may do a smaller grid to analyze the products. This table is a bit more abstract than the other representations as it does not include the individual products.

Number Cube 2

	×	Odd	Even
Number Cube 1	**Odd**	Odd	Even
	Even	Even	Even

For this reason, you may want to discuss it only if a student suggests it.

Suggested Questions If a student does raise it, two important questions are below.

- *Is each of the four cells in the grid equally likely?* (Yes, because odd and even are equally likely on each number cube.)

- *Where would the outcome (3, 4) be in this grid?* (In the upper right because the first number cube is odd, the second is even.)

Figure 1

Multiplication Game Results

If no one suggests using a chart like the one shown below to count the possible products, present the idea yourself, as it will be useful to have this sort of analysis handy for future work in the unit.

Number Cube 2

	1	2	3	4	5	6
1	1	2	3	4	5	6
2	2	4	6	8	10	12
3	3	6	9	12	15	18
4	4	8	12	16	20	24
5	5	10	15	20	25	30
6	6	12	18	24	30	36

(Number Cube 1 labels the rows.)

The class may want to spend a brief time looking at patterns that occur in the table.

Have the class discuss how the chart is useful for finding theoretical probabilities.

Suggested Questions Ask:

- *How do the experimental probabilities based on the class data compare to the theoretical probabilities?*

It is possible that the probabilities do not match. If that happens, ask:

- *Does this mean that there is something wrong with the collected data or with the theoretical probabilities?*

Students need to think and talk about the relationship between experimental probabilities and theoretical probabilities, continuing to question what each means and how each can be used to make sense of probability situations.

You can take this opportunity to connect number ideas with probability.

Suggested Questions With the chart displayed, you can ask questions about the probability of getting primes, factors, and multiples.

- *What is the probability of getting a product that is a multiple of 3?* ($\frac{20}{36}$ or $\frac{5}{9}$)

- *A product that is a multiple of 2 or 3?* ($\frac{32}{36}$ or $\frac{8}{9}$)

- *A product that is a factor of both 12 and 15?* ($\frac{2}{36}$ or $\frac{1}{18}$)

- *A product that is greater than 12?* ($\frac{13}{36}$)

The class may want to add their own questions to this list.

Suggested Question Ask students:

- *How can the game be made fair?*

Have some students explain their scoring rules for a new two-person game. Let the rest of the class check the proposed rules to be sure the game is fair. Students may change the rules of playing or scoring to make it a fair game.

1.3 Playing the Multiplication Game

Mathematical Goal

- Use probability and payoff to calculate the long-term average result of a game of chance

Launch

Refer to the Roller Derby Game in *How Likely Is It?* You could play a round of the game with the class. Pose a few questions about the probability of obtaining an even sum or an odd sum.

Introduce the Multiplication Game, and demonstrate a few rolls. After each roll, ask the class who scored on that roll. If the product of the two numbers shown is odd, Player A scores 1 point. If the product is even, Player B scores 1 point.

Ask students whether they think the game is fair and let them offer their conjectures.

Remind pairs that when they play the Multiplication Game, they will need to keep track of how many times each product is rolled and whether the product is even or odd.

- *When you compare your experimental probabilities to the theoretical probabilities, will they be exactly the same? Why or why not?*

Distribute two number cubes to each pair. Hand out Labsheet 1.3 for students to record their data.

Vocabulary
- Law of Large Numbers

Explore

Be on the lookout for students with interesting ways of thinking about how to compute the theoretical probabilities for this game.

Materials
- Labsheet 1.3
- Number cubes

Summarize

Begin with Question A, finding the experimental probabilities. Look at the data from a couple of the groups and then combine the data from all of the groups. Ask the class to compare the experimental probabilities from a small group and then from the entire class.

Make a line plot that shows the number of times each product came up as your students played the game.

Once the data from the entire class have been pooled, the class can compute the overall experimental probabilities to predict which products occur most often and whether or not the game is fair. Move to analyzing the theoretical probabilities. Discuss various strategies.

continued on next page

- *In the tree diagram, how is one roll of the number cubes represented? How is one roll represented in the chart? In the list?*

If no one suggests using a chart to count the possible products, present the idea yourself, as it will be useful to have this sort of analysis handy for future work in the unit. The class may want to spend a brief time looking at patterns that occur in the table. Discuss how the chart is useful for finding theoretical probabilities.

- *How do the experimental probabilities based on the class data compare to the theoretical probabilities?*

Finish by discussing the fairness of the game and whether it can be altered to be fair.

ACE Assignment Guide for Problem 1.3

Core 11, 12
Other *Applications* 13, *Connections* 23–28, *Extensions* 30–33; unassigned choices from previous problems

Adapted For suggestions about adapting ACE exercises, see the CMP *Special Needs Handbook*.

Answers to Problem 1.3

A. 1. Students will use various methods of recording data.

2. Answers will vary due to students' experimental results, but there should be roughly three times as many even as odd products.

B. 1. There are 18 distinct products. Each is listed below, followed in parentheses by the number of ways it can occur.

1 (1), 2 (2), 3 (2), 4 (3), 5 (2), 6 (4), 8 (2), 9 (1), 10 (2), 12 (4), 15 (2), 16 (1), 18 (2), 20 (2), 24 (2), 25 (1), 30 (2), 36 (1)

2. The 18 different products are not equally likely. Some products occur more than once. But each of the 36 outcomes is equally likely [e.g., while 4 is a more likely product than 1, the combination of (4, 1) is just as likely as (1, 1)].

3. $P(\text{odd product}) = \frac{1}{4}$; $P(\text{even product}) = \frac{27}{36}$.

C. In 100 trials, Player A could be expected to score 25 times (for 25 points) while Player B could be expected to score 75 times (for 75 points).

D. The game is not fair. Player B, who scores on even products, has a much greater chance of winning. You could change the rules. For example, Player A gets a point if the product is greater than or equal to 12 or the product is 1. Player B would win if the product is greater than or equal to 2 but less than 12. Note that this gives exactly 18 outcomes for each player. Another rule change is that Player A gets a point if the product is a multiple of 3 and Player B would get a point if the product is not a multiple of three. Students may decide to change the point assignments to 1 point per even product and 3 points per odd product. If the game is played many times, then this variation in point assignment would make the game fair. Each player could expect 27 points after 36 trials.

Evaluating Games of Chance

Many board games or computer games that you play involve chance. In some games, the square you land on depends on what numbers come up when you roll a pair of number cubes. Suppose you want to roll a sum of 10.

What is the probability that you will roll a sum of 10 on your turn?

In *How Likely Is It?*, you played the Roller Derby game, which involves finding the sum of two number cubes. You played the game several times and computed the **experimental probability** for each sum. To find the experimental probability of getting a sum of 10, you can use this formula:

$$P(\text{sum of 10}) = \frac{\text{number of times the sum of 10 occurred}}{\text{total number of trials}}$$

You also computed **theoretical probabilities** by listing all the possible outcomes. There are 36 outcomes, three of which result in a sum of 10.

What are the three ways in which you can get a sum of 10 when you roll a pair of number cubes?

The theoretical probability of getting a sum of 10 is

$$P(\text{sum of 10}) = \frac{\text{number of possible outcomes with a sum of 10}}{\text{total number of possible outcomes}} = \frac{3}{36} \text{ or } \frac{1}{12}$$

In this Investigation, you will explore several games involving chance. In each situation, you are asked to determine the chance, or probability, that certain outcomes will occur. In some situations, you will also be asked to determine whether a particular game is fair.

What do you think it means for a game to be fair?

Investigation 1 Evaluating Games of Chance   **5**

Notes _____

_____

_____

_____

1.1 Matching Colors

April and Tioko invented a two-player spinner game called Match/No-Match.

- Players take turns spinning a spinner like the one shown here.

- On each turn, a player spins the pointer of the spinner twice. If both spins land on the same color (a match), then Player A scores 1 point. If the two spins land on different colors (a no-match), then Player B scores 2 points.

- The player with the most points after 24 spins wins.

Do you think this is a fair or unfair game?

Are both players equally likely to win?

Problem 1.1 Experimental and Theoretical Probability

- Play the Match/No-Match game with a partner. Take a total of 24 turns (12 for each player).

- For each turn, record the color pair, for example, blue-yellow. Award points to the appropriate player.

online
For: Designer Dart Boards
Visit: PHSchool.com
Web Code: and-7101

A. Use the results you collect to find the experimental probabilities for a match and a no-match.

B. 1. List all of the possible outcomes of a turn (2 spins).

   2. Use the possible outcomes to determine the theoretical probability of a match and a no-match.

   3. Are the outcomes *equally likely*? That is, does each outcome have the same chance of occurring?

C. Compare the experimental and theoretical probabilities.

D. Is Match/No-Match a fair game? If it is fair, explain why. If it is not fair, explain how the rules can be changed to make the game fair.

ACE Homework starts on page 10.

6 What Do You Expect?

Notes _____

_____

_____

_____

1.2 Red and Blue Is a Winner!

In *How Likely Is It?*, you learned to find all the possible outcomes of a situation by making an organized list. April uses a tree diagram to show all the possible outcomes for the Match/No-Match game.

First, she lists the equally likely outcomes of the first spin.

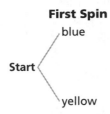

From each result of the first spin, April draws and labels two branches to show the possible results of the second spin.

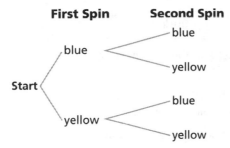

April can read all the possible outcomes of a turn by following the paths from left to right. For example, she can follow the upper branch from start to blue, and then from there, she can follow the upper branch to blue. This path represents the outcome blue-blue. The right column below lists the possible outcomes. The outcomes are all equally likely.

First Spin	Second Spin	Outcome
blue	blue	blue-blue
	yellow	blue-yellow
yellow	blue	yellow-blue
	yellow	yellow-yellow

Investigation 1 Evaluating Games of Chance   **7**

STUDENT PAGE

Notes _____

(7) 32

Problem 1.2 Using an Organized List

A carnival committee is considering using the Red and Blue game. The game involves choosing one marble at random from each of two buckets. The first bucket contains one green, one blue, one red, and one yellow marble. The second bucket contains one green, one red, and one yellow marble.

Without looking, a player chooses one marble from each bucket in the Red and Blue game. If the player gets a red and a blue marble (the order makes no difference), the player wins. Each player pays $1 to play and receives $3 for each win.

Bucket 1   **Bucket 2**

A. Before playing the game, do you predict that the school will make money on this game? Explain.

B. Make a tree diagram to show the possible outcomes for this game. Explain how your tree shows all the possible outcomes.

C. What is the theoretical probability of choosing a red and blue marble on a turn?

D. Suppose the game is played 36 times.

  1. How much money can the school expect to collect?

  2. How much money can the school expect to pay out to the winners?

  3. Did the school make money? If so, how much?

E. Suppose one marble is chosen from each bucket. Find the probability of each situation.

  1. You choose a green marble from Bucket 1 and a yellow marble from Bucket 2.

  2. You do *not* choose a blue marble from either bucket.

  3. You choose two blue marbles.

  4. You choose at least one blue marble.

ACE **Homework starts on page 10.**

Notes

_____

_____

_____

_____

1.3 Playing the Multiplication Game

You have played games that use the sum of two number cubes. In the following game, scoring depends on the *product* of the numbers rolled.

Problem 1.3 Determining Whether a Game Is Fair

Multiplication Game Rules

- Player A and Player B take turns rolling two number cubes.
- If the product of the numbers rolled is odd, Player A wins a point. If the product of the numbers rolled is even, Player B wins a point.
- The player with the most points after 36 rolls wins.

Multiplication Game
SCORE

Player A	Player B

A. 1. Play the Multiplication Game with a partner for a total of 36 turns. Keep track of your results.

2. Based on your data, what is the experimental probability of rolling an odd product? What is the probability of an even product?

B. 1. List the possible products. In how many different ways can each product occur?

2. Is each product equally likely? Explain.

3. What is the theoretical probability of rolling an odd product? What is the theoretical probability of rolling an even product?

C. Suppose the game has 100 rolls instead of 36. How many points do you expect each player to have at the end of the game?

D. Do you think the Multiplication Game is fair? Explain. If the game is not fair, explain how the rules could be changed so that the game is fair.

ACE Homework starts on page 10.

Notes _____

_____

_____

_____

Applications

1. Decide whether the possible resulting events are equally likely. Explain.

Action	Possible resulting events
a. You roll a number cube.	You roll an even number, or you roll an odd number.

b. A young child grows.	The child is left-handed, or the child is right-handed.
c. You toss a marshmallow.	The marshmallow lands on its end, or the marshmallow lands on its curved side.

d. You choose a card from a standard deck of 52 playing cards with no jokers.	The card is a heart, the card is a club, the card is a diamond, or the card is a spade.
e. You toss a coin three times.	You get three heads, two heads and a tail, a head and two tails, or three tails.

2. Lori's little sister Emily tore the labels from ten cans of vegetables. Now all the cans look exactly the same. Three cans are corn, two are spinach, four are beans, and one is tomatoes. Lori picks a can at random. Find each probability.

   a. P(corn) **b.** P(beans)

   c. P(not spinach) **d.** P(beans or tomatoes)

   e. Is each vegetable equally likely to be in the can? Explain.

For: Multiple-Choice Skills Practice
Web Code: ana-7154

Notes _____

_____

_____

_____

3. Jacob has a probability party. He serves three items, each item selected at random from two options. Each guest gets a hamburger or a hot dog, cole slaw or potato salad, and an apple or an orange.

   a. Make a tree diagram to show all possibilities.

   b. What is the probability that Samantha gets a hot dog, cole slaw, and an orange?

   c. Rick does not like hot dogs. What is the probability that he will *not* be served a hot dog?

4. José is going to a party. He decides to wear his jeans and a sweater, but he hasn't decided what else to wear. The tree diagram shows the possible outfits he can make if he chooses sneakers or loafers; a pair of blue, red, or white socks; and a green, red, or plaid cap, at random.

   a. What is the probability that José will wear loafers, blue socks, and a plaid cap?

   b. What is the probability that José will wear sneakers, either red or blue socks, and a green cap?

   c. What is the probability that José will wear neither red socks nor a red cap?

Investigation 1 Evaluating Games of Chance   **11**

Notes _____

_____

_____

_____

For Exercises 5–9, Monita and Kyan are analyzing a game involving two different spinners. A turn is one spin on each spinner. They make this tree diagram of equally likely outcomes to find theoretical probabilities.

5. Multiple Choice Choose the spinner that could be Spinner X.

A.

B.

C.

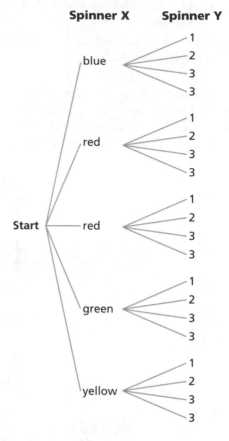

D. None of these is correct.

6. List all possible outcomes of spinning each spinner, Spinner X and Spinner Y, once.

7. Which color and number combination has the greatest probability of occurring?

8. What is the probability of getting red on Spinner X and 3 on Spinner Y?

9. What is the probability of *not* getting a 3 on Spinner Y?

STUDENT PAGE

Notes _____

_____

_____

_____

10. In the Gee Whiz Everyone Wins! game show, members of the audience choose a block at random from the bucket shown at the right. If a blue block is chosen, the contestant wins $5. If a red block is chosen, the contestant wins $10. If the yellow block is chosen, the contestant wins $50. The block is replaced after each turn.

   a. What is the probability of choosing each color? Explain your method.

   b. Suppose 24 contestants choose and replace a block. How much money can the game show expect to pay out?

11. In Raymundo's Prime Number Multiplication Game, a player rolls two number cubes. Player A gets 10 points if the product is prime. Player B gets 1 point if the product is not prime. Raymundo thinks this scoring system is reasonable because there are many more ways to roll a non-prime product than a prime product.

   a. If the cubes are rolled 100 times, how many points would you expect Player A to score? How many points would you expect Player B to score?

   b. Is Raymundo's game a fair game? Explain.

12. Rachel says that if she rolls two number cubes 36 times, she will get a product of 1 exactly once. Mariana said that she cannot be sure this will happen exactly once, but it will probably happen very few times. Who is right? Explain your reasoning.

13. Rachel told Mariana that if she rolls two number cubes 100 times, she will never get a product of 23. Mariana told her that she can't be sure. Who is right? Explain.

Notes _____

_____

_____

_____

Connections

14. The probability of an event is a number between 0 (0%) and 1 (100%). The larger the probability, the greater the chances the event will occur. If an event is impossible, the probability that it will occur is 0 (or 0%). If an event is certain to happen, the probability that it will occur is 1, or 100%.

Copy the scale below. Place the letter of each event a–i on the scale at the spot that best describes its probability.

Impossible   Certain

0.0   0.5   1.0

a. You get a head when you toss a coin.

b. You run 20 miles in one hour.

c. You roll a 6 on a number cube.

d. Your neighbor's cat has four legs.

e. The sun will rise tomorrow.

f. You toss a coin twice and get two heads.

g. You toss a coin twice and get at least one head.

h. You listen to a CD today.

i. You spin the spinner below, and it lands on red.

15. **Multiple Choice** What fraction of this diagram is shaded?

Homework Help Online
PHSchool.com

For: Help with Exercise 15
Web Code: ane-7115

F. $\frac{1}{2}$ G. $\frac{2}{5}$ H. $\frac{1}{3}$ J. $\frac{4}{9}$

STUDENT PAGE

Notes _____

_____

_____

_____

16. Write three fractions equivalent to the fraction you chose in Exercise 15.

17. Multiple Choice What fraction of this diagram is shaded?

A. $\frac{20}{100}$ **B.** $\frac{4}{8}$ **C.** $\frac{1}{2}$ **D.** $\frac{1}{4}$

18. Write three fractions equivalent to the fraction you chose in Exercise 17.

19. Fala spins this spinner several times. The table shows the results.

  a. How many times did Fala spin the spinner?

  b. What percent of the spins landed in the blue region? What percent landed in the yellow region?

  c. According to the theoretical probabilities, what is the percent of the spins expected to land in the blue region over the long run? In the yellow region?

  d. Compare the experimental probability of the spinner landing in each region with the theoretical probability. If the probabilities are different, explain why.

STUDENT PAGE

Notes _____

_____

_____

_____

20. If you drop a tack on the floor, there are two possible outcomes: the tack lands on its side (point down), or the tack lands on its head (point up). Kalifa dropped a tack 100 times. The table shows the results.

point down   point up

Outcomes	Number of Times It Occurs
Tack lands point up	58
Tack lands point down	42

a. Suppose you drop Kalifa's tack 500 times. How many times do you expect it to land point up?

b. Is it equally likely that the tack will land point up or point down? Explain.

c. Is it possible to determine theoretical probabilities for this situation? Why or why not?

21. Juanita is deciding whether to play a game at an amusement park. It takes one ticket to play the game. A player tosses two plastic bottles. If both bottles land standing up, the player wins ten tickets to use for rides and games. Juanita watches people play and records the results.

Both land on side	One lands on side and one lands standing up	Both land standing up
ⅼⅼⅼⅼⅼ ⅼⅼⅼⅼⅼ ⅼⅼⅼⅼⅼ ⅼⅼⅼⅼⅼ ⅼⅼⅼⅼ	ⅼⅼⅼⅼⅼ ⅼⅼⅼⅼⅼ ⅼⅼⅼⅼ	ⅼⅼ

a. Based on Juanita's results, what is the experimental probability of winning the game?

b. Suppose Juanita plays this game 20 times. How many times can she expect to win?

16   What Do You Expect?

Notes _____

_____

_____

_____

c. How many tickets can Juanita expect to be ahead or behind after playing the game 20 times? Explain your reasoning.

d. Is it possible to find the theoretical probability of winning this game? Why or why not?

22. A bucket contains 60 marbles. Some are red, some are blue, and some are white. The probability of drawing a red marble is 35%. The probability of drawing a blue marble is 25%. How many marbles of each color are in the bucket?

23. Hannah's teacher brought in a bucket containing 72 blocks. The blocks are red, yellow, or blue. Hannah wants to figure out the number of blue blocks without emptying the bucket.

Hannah chooses a block from the bucket, records its color, and then replaces it. Of her 14 draws, she records blue 5 times. Based on Hannah's experiment, how many of the blocks are blue? Explain.

24. Suppose you roll two number cubes. What is the probability that the product of the numbers will be a multiple of 5?

25. If you roll two number cubes 100 times, about how many times can you expect the product of the numbers to be a multiple of 5?

26. Suppose you roll two number cubes. What is the probability that the product of the numbers is a multiple of 7?

27. If you roll two number cubes a million times, about how many times can you expect the product of the numbers to be a multiple of 7?

28. Suppose you roll two number cubes and multiply the numbers. Find each probability.

a. P(product is a multiple of 3 and 4)

b. P(product is a multiple of 3 or 4)

c. P(product has a factor of 5 and 3)

d. P(product is a prime number)

e. P(product is greater than 10)

f. P(product is less than 18)

Notes _____

_____

_____

_____

Extensions

29. Tricia wants to determine the probability of getting two 1's when two number cubes are rolled. She makes a tree diagram and uses it to list the possible outcomes.

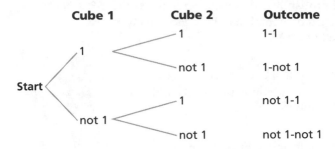

| Cube 1 | Cube 2 | Outcome |

She says that, because there are four possible outcomes, the probability of getting 1 on both number cubes is $\frac{1}{4}$. Is Tricia right? Explain.

30. Juan invented a two-person game in which players take turns rolling three number cubes. If the sum is even, Player A gets a point. If the sum is odd, Player B gets a point. Is Juan's game a fair game? Explain.

For Exercises 31–33, a computer places a dot at random on each dartboard below.

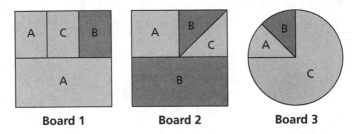

Board 1   Board 2   Board 3

31. For each dartboard, what is the probability that a dot will be in a region marked A? A region marked B? A region marked C?

32. For Board 1, what is the probability that a dot will be in a region marked A or B?

33. For Board 2, what is the probability that a dot will *not* be in region C?

Notes _____

_____

_____

_____

Mathematical Reflections 1

In this investigation, you explored games of chance. Working on the problems gave you an opportunity to review ideas about experimental and theoretical probability. The following questions will help you summarize what you have learned.

Think about your answers to these questions. Discuss your ideas with other students and your teacher. Then write a summary of your findings in your notebook.

1. **a.** Compare experimental and theoretical probabilities.

   b. Describe some strategies you can use to find experimental probabilities.

   c. Describe some strategies you can use to find theoretical probabilities.

2. How do you use probabilities, either theoretical or experimental, to decide if a particular game of chance is fair?

3. In a game of chance, how can you predict the number of times out of 100 a given outcome will occur?

Notes _____

_____

_____

_____

Investigation ❶

ACE
Assignment Choices

Differentiated Instruction
Solutions for All Learners

Problem 1.1
Core 1, 2, 15–18
Other *Connections* 14, 19

Problem 1.2
Core 3, 10, 22
Other *Applications* 4–9; *Connections* 20, 21; *Extensions* 29; unassigned choices from previous problems

Problem 1.3
Core 11, 12
Other *Applications* 13, *Connections* 23–28, *Extensions* 30–33; unassigned choices from previous problems

Adapted For suggestions about adapting Exercise 10 and other ACE exercises, see the CMP *Special Needs Handbook*.
Connecting to Prior Units 14: *Bits and Pieces I*

Applications

1. **a.** The outcomes are equally likely, as there are three ways to roll an even number (2, 4, and 6) and three ways to roll an odd number (1, 3, and 5), and each number is equally likely.

   b. The outcomes are probably not equally likely, as handedness is not evenly distributed and probably depends on genetics and social influence.

   c. The outcomes are probably not equally likely; explanations will vary, but experiments have shown that a tossed marshmallow is more likely to land on its side than on its end.

   d. The outcomes are equally likely, as there are 13 cards of each suit in a deck.

   e. The outcomes are not equally likely, as there is only one way to get three heads (HHH), three ways to get two heads (HHT, HTH, and THH), three ways to get two tails (TTH, THT, and HTT), and one way to get three tails (TTT).

2. **a.** $\frac{3}{10}$ or 0.3

   b. $\frac{4}{10}$ or 0.4

   c. $\frac{8}{10}$ or 0.8

   d. $\frac{5}{10}$ or 0.5

   e. No; the probabilities that the can contains each vegetable are not the same, so the vegetables are not equally likely to be in the can. *P*(beans) is the greatest.

3. **a.**

   b. There are eight different outcomes. The probability of a hot dog, cole slaw, and an orange is $\frac{1}{8}$.

   c. There are eight outcomes; four of which do not have a hot dog. The probability of no hot dog is $\frac{4}{8}$.

4. **Note:** Some teachers have found it useful to photocopy the diagram in the Student Edition as a Labsheet for students.

   a. The probability that José will choose any one of the 18 possible combinations is $\frac{1}{18}$.

   b. $\frac{2}{18}$ or $\frac{1}{9}$

   c. $\frac{8}{18}$ or $\frac{4}{9}$

5. B

6. blue–1, blue–2, blue–3, blue–3, red–1, red–2, red–3, red–3, red–1, red–2, red–3, red–3, green–1, green–2, green–3, green–3, yellow–1, yellow–2, yellow–3, yellow–3

7. red–3 (It can occur four different ways.)

8. $\frac{4}{20}$ or $\frac{1}{5}$

9. $\frac{10}{20}$ or $\frac{1}{2}$

10. a. $P(\text{red}) = \frac{2}{6} = \frac{1}{3}$, $P(\text{blue}) = \frac{3}{6} = \frac{1}{2}$, $P(\text{yellow}) = \frac{1}{6}$

   b. Of 24 contestants, the game show could expect 12 to choose blue ($\frac{1}{2}$ of 24), 8 to choose red ($\frac{1}{3}$ of 24), and 4 to choose yellow ($\frac{1}{6}$ of 24), an expected payout of $\$5(12) + \$10(8) + \$50(4) = \$340$.

11. a. The prime products are 2, 3, and 5 and can be obtained 6 different ways. The probability of getting a prime product is thus $\frac{6}{36}$ or $\frac{1}{6}$. Out of 100 rolls, Player A can expect a prime number about $\frac{1}{6}$ of the time, or about 17 times, earning about 170 points. Player B can expect a nonprime product about $\frac{1}{6}$ of the time, or about 83 times, earning about 83 points.

   b. Raymundo's game is not fair. Player A can expect to score about twice as many points as Player B. (To make the game fair, Player A could score 5 points for every prime product.)

12. Mariana is right. Rachel is assuming that the theoretical probabilities will always hold true. The theoretical probability of $\frac{1}{36}$ for rolling a product of 1 means that a product of 1 can be expected to happen about once in every 36 rolls. With such a small number of trials, it is quite possible for a product of 1 to be rolled more than once or not to be rolled at all.

13. Rachel is right. The number 23 is prime and could only be obtained by rolling a 1 and a 23, which is impossible.

Connections

14.

The placement of the letter h will vary.

15. J

16. Possible answers: $\frac{8}{18}, \frac{12}{27}, \frac{16}{36}$

17. A

18. Possible answers: $\frac{1}{5}, \frac{2}{10}, \frac{10}{50}, \frac{40}{200}$

19. a. 25 times

   b. 36% landed in the blue region; 64% landed in the yellow region.

   c. Theoretically, the spinner should land on blue 25% of the time and yellow 75% of the time.

   d. The experimental and the theoretical probabilities differ. Possible explanation: A theoretical probability, if based on many trials, tells you about what to expect, but 25 is not a large number of spins. With more spins, the experimental probabilities would probably be closer to the theoretical probabilities.

   Some students might explain the results in terms of bias. For example, they might say that his desk was tipped slightly in the direction of the blue area on the spinner. This is a reasonable explanation, but it is also important for students to understand that not every difference between theoretical and experimental probabilities is the result of bias.

20. a. This tack could be expected to land point up 58% of the 500 times, or about 290 times.

   b. Based on the experimental probabilities given, the two outcomes are probably not equally likely. However, we cannot be certain without computing theoretical probabilities or conducting a very large number of trials.

c. We cannot figure out the theoretical probabilities for this experiment (though a theoretical physicist might be able to do so!) because it is too complex.

21. a. $\frac{2}{40}$ or $\frac{1}{20}$

b. She could expect to win about once, since the experimental probability of winning is $\frac{1}{20}$.

c. It would take 20 tickets for Juanita to play 20 times, and her one expected win would earn her 10 tickets, so she can expect to be behind 10 tickets.

d. The various outcomes are not equally likely and the situation is very complex, so it is probably impossible to find the theoretical probability of winning. It also probably varies with the skill of the thrower.

22. red: 35% of 60 is 21 marbles; blue: 25% of 60 is 15 marbles; white: $60 - 36$ is 24 marbles.

23. Five choices out of 14 is about 36%, and 36% of 72 blocks is about 26 blocks. However, 14 choices are not enough to make a good prediction of the number of blue blocks in the bucket.

24. $\frac{11}{36}$

25. $\frac{11}{36} \times 100 =$ about 31 times

26. 0

27. 0; you can never roll a multiple of 7.

28. a. $\frac{7}{36}$ **b.** $\frac{28}{36}$ **c.** $\frac{4}{36} = \frac{1}{9}$

    d. $\frac{6}{36} = \frac{1}{6}$ **e.** $\frac{17}{36}$ **f.** $\frac{26}{36} = \frac{13}{18}$

Extensions

29. The way Tricia has constructed her tree diagram, the four outcomes are not equally likely. This leads to her incorrect reasoning that the probability of getting a 1 on both number cubes is $\frac{1}{4}$. In fact, there are 36 possible equally likely outcomes for a roll of two number cubes, and only one is (1, 1), so the probability is actually $\frac{1}{36}$.

30. Making a tree diagram for this situation would be quite cumbersome, given the 216 outcomes. With two number cubes, the probabilities for rolling an odd or an even sum are equal. The third number cube could

come up either odd or even, with equal probability. If it is even, the previous even sums stay even and the odd sums stay odd. If it is odd, the previous even sums become odd and the odd sums become even. The split between odd and even sums stays the same, making Juan's game fair.

31. Board 1: $P(A) = \frac{2}{3}$; $P(B) = \frac{1}{6}$; $P(C) = \frac{1}{6}$

Board 2: $P(A) = \frac{1}{4}$; $P(B) = \frac{5}{8}$; $P(C) = \frac{1}{8}$

Board 3: $P(A) = \frac{1}{8}$; $P(B) = \frac{1}{8}$; $P(C) = \frac{3}{4}$

32. $\frac{5}{6}$

33. $\frac{7}{8}$

Possible Answers to Mathematical Reflections

1. a. An experimental probability is a probability based on data from conducting an experiment. If the experiment is conducted several times for a small number of trials, one is likely to get several different experimental probabilities. However, if each experiment involves a large number of trials, the experimental probabilities will be very close to each other. A theoretical probability is what can be expected to happen if an experiment is carried out many times. Theoretical probabilities are found by using math to analyze the situation rather than experimenting.

b. Experimental probabilities are found by conducting many trials and then dividing the number of times a desired outcome occurred by the number of trials. In this investigation spinners, marbles in a bucket, or number cubes were used to conduct an experiment.

c. Tree diagrams can be used to list all the possible outcomes. Sometimes we just made lists by thinking about the possible outcomes. Also a grid or chart like the one used in finding the product of two rolls of a number cube can be used.

2. A game of chance is fair if each of the players has the same probability of scoring a given number of points. In the long run, every player should expect to win the same number of points.

3. To predict the number of times an outcome will occur, find either a theoretical probability (if that is possible) or an experimental probability. To find the number of times an outcome will occur using a theoretical probability, one first needs to determine the probability that the outcome will occur. To do this, make a table, a tree diagram, chart, or an organized list of possible outcomes. Then, multiply the probability by 100. For instance, the probability of rolling double sixes with two number cubes is $\frac{1}{36}$, so the number of double sixes expected in 100 rolls is:

$$\frac{1}{36} \times 100 = \frac{100}{36} = 2\frac{28}{36} \approx 3.$$

To find an experimental probability, gather enough data to be able to make a good guess about the probability. The more data gathered, the closer the experimental probability will be to the theoretical probability. Then, multiply this probability by 100.

Alternatively, the probability can be expressed as a percent. Because percent means *out of 100*, the percentage is the number of times out of 100 the outcome is expected to occur.

Investigation 2 — Analyzing Situations Using an Area Model

Mathematical and Problem-Solving Goals

- Use an area model to analyze the theoretical probabilities for two-stage outcomes

- Simulate and analyze probability situations involving two-stage outcomes

- Distinguish between equally likely and non–equally likely outcomes by collecting data and analyzing experimental probabilities

Summary of Problems

Problem 2.1 Making Purple

Students are introduced to an area model for analyzing probabilities with two-stage outcomes.

Problem 2.2 Choosing Paths

In a new context, students continue to study multi-stage outcomes. Students design simulations to determine the experimental probabilities of ending up in each of two rooms at the end of a series of paths with forks.

Problem 2.3 Finding the Best Arrangement

Students again use an area model to find theoretical probabilities in a novel context. In the previous problems, the second stage has been similar to the first stage, spinning the pointer of a second spinner or making a second choice along a path. In this case, the two stages of the outcome are of a different nature from each other.

	Suggested Pacing	Materials for Students	Materials for Teachers	ACE Assignments
All	4 days		Transparencies for 2.1 to 2.3 and transparency markers	
2.1	1 day	Labsheet 2.1 (1 per pair); bobby pins or paper clips (for spinners, 1 per pair)	Transparency 2.1A (optional); Transparency 2.1B	1, 2, 3, 13, 14, 25
2.2	$1\frac{1}{2}$ days	Number cubes (1 cube per pair); colored blocks, coins; large sheets of paper and markers (optional)	Transparencies 2.2A and 2.2B	4–7, 15–22, 26
2.3	1 day	Two identical opaque containers (per group); colored blocks or marbles (two of each of two colors per group)	Transparency 2.3 (optional)	8–12, 23, 24, 27, 28
MR	$\frac{1}{2}$ day			

2.1

Making Purple

Goal

- Use an area model to analyze the theoretical probabilities for two-stage outcomes

This problem involves spinning two spinners that are subdivided into sections labeled with different color names. If one spinner comes up red and the other blue, then the color purple is made and the player is a winner. An area model is used to analyze the theoretical probability for the situation.

Launch 2.1

Demonstrate how to analyze a two-stage outcome using an area model. The student edition uses Problem 1.2 to demonstrate the method.

Alternatively, you could first play the Making Purple game to determine experimental probabilities and then, with the whole class, demonstrate how to determine theoretical probabilities using an area model.

Describe the Making Purple game to the class. Demonstrate one or two turns on the two spinners using Transparency 2.1B, if possible.

Suggested Question Ask:

- *Do you think purple and not purple are equally likely outcomes?*

Most students will intuitively know that the two outcomes are not equally likely but they may not be sure how to find the probability of making purple. Some may think that the probability of making purple is $\frac{1}{3} + \frac{1}{6}$ because one spinner is divided into thirds and the other into sixths. Others may offer other suggestions. Again, don't confirm or refute their conjectures. These ideas will be revisited in the summary.

Let students work in pairs.

Explore 2.1

Circulate as pairs work, assisting those who are having trouble analyzing this two-stage game. The problem asks many questions similar to those asked in Investigation 1. Revisiting these questions gives

you a chance to help students who are still struggling with these ideas.

Suggested Questions Some students may need help in labeling and interpreting the area model. Rather than show them again, ask them some questions.

- *For spinner A, what are the probabilities of getting each color?* ($\frac{1}{6}$ for blue, yellow, and green and $\frac{3}{6}$ for red.)

- *How can you represent this on the square?* (Divide the square into six equal regions.)

- *Label each of the regions green, blue, red, or yellow.*

Note that students can subdivide the square starting from the left side or the top side. It makes no difference, but for ease in comparing student work in the summary, encourage the students to start with the left side of the square.

- *For spinner B, what are the probabilities of getting each color?* ($\frac{1}{3}$)

- *How can you represent this on the square?* (Subdivide the square into three equal parts starting with the top side of the square.)

- *How many regions do you have?* (18)

- *What does each region represent?* (The results of two spins.)

- *Label each region with the outcome it represents.* (RB, RY, etc.)

- *Which regions represent purple?* (Those labeled RB or BR.)

- *What is the probability of getting purple?*

- *What are some other probabilities for this game?*

Going Further

For those who finish early, ask:

- *What if you have a choice of spinning each spinner once or of spinning one spinner twice? Is the probability of getting purple still the same? Explain.*

Summarize 2.1

Begin with Question A. Elicit students' strategies for finding the experimental probabilities for making purple. To find the experimental probabilities, students analyze their data, count the number of times purple was made, and write a ratio that compares this amount to the total number of trials.

Before discussing the theoretical probabilities, ask what other strategies could be used to determine the outcomes. Some students may try to use a list. Some may try a tree.

Call on one or two students to demonstrate how they found the theoretical probabilities. Compare these with the experimental probabilities.

Discuss Question D. Suggest a number of players other than 36. Ask the class to answer the questions in Question D using this number. Or, have each group pick a different number and then answer the questions.

- *Compare your answers using this new number of players to the answers you got for 36 players.*

For example, suppose 72 players played the game. The school still makes a profit, but it is larger, $48 rather than $24. The school can expect to make about $0.67 on average for each player. This is the same no matter how many players play the game.

Check for Understanding

You could display two sets of spinners like those below and ask students to decide which set is more likely to make purple. In this instance, the two sets have the same probability of making purple, namely $\frac{1}{4}$.

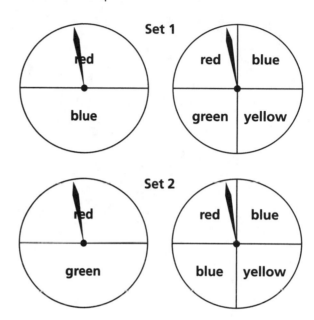

Mathematical Goal

- Use an area model to analyze the theoretical probabilities for two-stage outcomes

Launch

Demonstrate how to analyze a two-stage outcome using an area model. Alternatively, play the Making Purple game to determine experimental probabilities and then demonstrate how to determine theoretical probabilities using the area model.

Describe the Making Purple game to the class. Demonstrate one or two turns on the two spinners. Ask:

- *Do you think* purple *and* not purple *are equally likely outcomes?*

Let students work in pairs.

Materials

- Transparency 2.1A
- Transparency 2.1B

Vocabulary

- area model

Explore

As pairs work, assist those who are having trouble analyzing this two-stage game.

Some students may need help in labeling and interpreting the area model. Ask questions about the model.

- *For spinner A, what are the probabilities of getting each color?*
- *How can you represent this on the square?*

As a challenge for those who finish early, consider the following question.

- *What if you have a choice of spinning each spinner once or of spinning one spinner twice? Is the probability of getting purple still the same? Explain.*

Materials

- Labsheet 2.1
- Bobby pins or paper clips

Summarize

Begin with Question A. Elicit students' strategies for finding the experimental probabilities for making purple.

Before discussing the theoretical probabilities, ask what other strategies could be used to determine the outcomes. Compare the theoretical probabilities to the experimental probabilities.

Discuss Question D. Suggest a number of players other than 36. Ask the class to answer the questions in Question D using this number.

- *Compare your answers using this new number of players to the answers you got for 36 players.*

Materials

- Student notebooks

continued on next page

Check for Understanding

You could display two sets of spinners like those on page 39 of the Teacher's Guide and ask students to decide which set is more likely to make purple. In this instance, the two sets have the same probability of making purple, namely $\frac{1}{4}$.

ACE Assignment Guide for Problem 2.1

Core 2, 3

Other *Applications* 1; *Connections* 13, 14; *Extensions* 25

Adapted For suggestions about adapting ACE exercises, see the CMP *Special Needs Handbook*.
Connecting to Prior Units Exercise 13: *Data About Us*; Exercise 14: *Accentuate the Negative*

Answers to Problem 2.1

A. Answers will vary. Some may be close to $\frac{4}{18}$ or $\frac{2}{9}$.

B. The diagram below is a correct area model. The shaded portions represent the ways to get purple with the two spinners. $P(\text{purple}) = \frac{4}{18}$.

C. They are not necessarily the same. However, they may be close to each other due to the number of times the game was played.

D. 1. The school will take in $72 from this game.

2. The school would expect to pay $48 for prizes.

3. The school would expect to make $24 from this game.

	Spinner 2		
	Green	**Red**	**Blue**
Red			▓
Red			▓
Red			▓
Green			
Blue		▓	
Yellow			

Spinner 1

2.2 Choosing Paths

Goals

- Simulate and analyze probability situations involving two-stage outcomes

- Distinguish between equally likely and non-equally likely outcomes by collecting data and analyzing experimental probabilities

- Use an area model to analyze the theoretical probabilities for two-stage outcomes

Problem 2.2 introduces a new probability context, that of analyzing paths in a game. At various places along the paths, students must choose a path at random until they end up in one of two rooms. Students first simulate the game and assign probabilities using their simulation. An area model is then used to determine the theoretical probabilities.

Launch 2.2

Introduce the Choosing Paths game. Display the game screen, which is shown on Transparency 2.2A. Use the Getting Ready to help the class focus on how the game is played and how to use a number cube to help make decisions at each split in the path.

Suggested Questions

- *Are you more likely to end in Cave A or in Cave B? Why?* (Some students may say Cave B because it is larger; some may say the caves have an equal chance of being entered because three paths lead into each room; some may say Cave A because the middle path leads directly into this cave.)

To help students better understand the paths, you could cover up all of the diagram after the first split in the path, as below:

- *Suppose you are playing the game and have to make a random decision at the first split in the path about which part of the path (upper, middle or lower) to follow. How can a number cube help?* (You could take the upper if 1 or 2 is rolled, the middle if 3 or 4 is rolled, and the lower if 5 or 6 is rolled.)

- *Does this give each of the paths the same chance of being chosen?* (Yes.)

- *What is the probability of selecting each one of these three paths?* ($\frac{1}{3}$)

Now move the paper to reveal the upper paths and again ask the question.

- *How can you use the number cube to help you decide which path to take if each is to have an equal chance?* (Let the upper path be selected if a 1, 2, or 3 is rolled and the lower selected if a 4, 5, or 6 is rolled.)

- *What is the probability of selecting one of these paths?* ($\frac{1}{2}$ for each fork of the path)

Now focus on ways to simulate the maze.

- *How can we simulate walking through the maze and choosing paths at random?*

- *Random means that you can't choose paths by picking your favorite number or your favorite direction. At each fork, every path must have exactly the same probability of being chosen. The number cube will be our way to make decisions at random at each split in a path.*

- *Let's play a version of the game in our class. Let's pretend to walk through the maze choosing paths at random.*

- *At each fork or intersection, you must choose a path in such a way that each path has exactly the same probability of being selected.*

Play the game a couple of times or until everyone understands how it is played.

Have number cubes for groups to use to generate random choices.

- *In your group carry out the experiment 18 times and answer Questions A and B. Then, move on to Questions C–E.*

Play the game 18 times and record group results.

Suggested Question As groups work, ask questions about what they are discovering.

- *Which cave seems to have the greater probability of the player entering it? What makes you think this?*

- *If you come to a fork that splits into three paths, what probability does each path have of being selected?*

- *Suppose your first choice is to take one of three paths, each of which is followed by a choice of two paths. What is the probability that you will take any given second path?*

When students move to the area model analysis to find a theoretical probability model, some students may try to label the top of the diagram as they did in 2.1. Here labels do not work because each path may have different probabilities. The better way is to reallocate the area allotted to a path into as many equal-sized parts as there are forks in the path (2, 0, or 3) as you read from the upper path to middle path to the lower path. At this stage the diagram should look like the following:

- *After the first division, what fraction of the total area of the square does each of the three paths represent?*

Now the students can make a diagram to show where you end for each of the options to get the following:

- *Now that we have divided a square to represent the different paths, what fraction should we assign to each part of the square?*

- *What is the probability of landing in Cave A? In Cave B?*

As students work on Question E, have them put their path game on a large sheet of paper with the outcomes and probabilities for entering each cave.

Collect groups' strategies for walking the maze and making random path choices at each fork. Be sure to have the class confirm that these strategies make sense.

Have students share the experimental probabilities they found for each cave. Discuss reasons for variation in the data. Ask questions about other ways to make random choices at each split in the path. Help the class to pool their experimental data and to calculate the experimental probabilities based on all the groups' trials. Save the experimental data to compare with the theoretical data in Question C.

Ask students how their experimental probability compared to their initial idea about the cave in which they would end.

Now move the students to Question C and look at examples of the area diagrams the students complete. Use the diagrams in the Explore as a guide.

- *How did you assign probabilities to ending in Cave A or in Cave B?* (There were three different areas assigned to each cave.

Cave A: $\frac{1}{6} + \frac{1}{3} + \frac{1}{9} = \frac{11}{18}$

Cave B: $\frac{1}{6} + \frac{1}{9} + \frac{1}{9} = \frac{7}{18}$

Some groups will partition the grid into equal-sized parts in order to find the probabilities. Partitioning into 18 parts is shown below.)

Another way to think about this is to write a number sentence for each probability and have the class connect the number sentence back to the area model. For example, the probability of landing in Cave B is: $\left(\frac{1}{3}\right)\left(\frac{1}{2}\right) + \left(\frac{1}{3}\right)\left(\frac{1}{3}\right) + \left(\frac{1}{3}\right)\left(\frac{1}{3}\right) = \frac{1}{6} + \frac{1}{9} + \frac{1}{9} = \frac{7}{18}$.

Choosing a way to simulate random events related to a particular problem is important. Discuss with your class other strategies that could have been used to simulate the path game.

Suggested Questions Ask:

- *Look back at the simulation we used to find the experimental probabilities of ending in Cave A or B. We used a number cube. Could we have used a spinner? If so, how?* (A six-section spinner can work just like a number cube. But we could also use several spinners depending on how many equally likely choices we have to make. In this game we could use two spinners, one with three equal parts and one with two equal parts. Then you just spin the spinner that matches the number of choices.)

- *What are some other ideas about how to simulate the path game?* (Students might suggest colored cubes in buckets, pieces of paper labeled with choices, or other random devices.)

Note: Using the area model provides practice with writing equivalent fractions, adding, and multiplying fractions. Subdividing the square twice is a model for multiplication of fractions that students studied in the sixth-grade unit, *Bits and Pieces II*. This is an opportunity to assess students' facility with fractions.

Mathematics Background

For background on multiplying probabilities, see page 5.

Compare the theoretical and experimental probabilities.

For Question E, you can post the path games that the students created around the cave. You can either have the class explain their paths or have the class move around in groups to check one or two of the paths to see if they match the given analysis. Ask what strategies they used.

Check for Understanding

For a further check on whether students understand how to find the probabilities of successive events, draw another maze for the class to analyze. For example, this maze is shown on Transparency 2.2B.

Give the class some time to think about this example. The associated area model for the example might look as follows:

Upper Path	B	B	A
Middle Path		A	
Lower Path	A	B	B

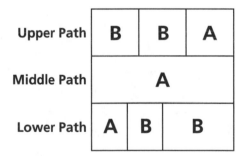

Adding the fractional parts of the drawing that represent ending in each cave gives

$\frac{1}{9} + \frac{1}{3} + \frac{1}{12} = \frac{19}{36}$ for Cave A and

$\frac{1}{9} + \frac{1}{9} + \frac{1}{12} + \frac{1}{6} = \frac{17}{36}$ for Cave B.

2.2 Choosing Paths

Mathematical Goals

- Simulate and analyze probability situations involving two-stage outcomes
- Distinguish between equally likely and non–equally likely outcomes by collecting data and analyzing experimental probabilities
- Use an area model to analyze the theoretical probabilities for two-stage outcomes

Launch

Display the Choosing Paths game screen shown on Transparency 2.2A. Use the Getting Ready to focus on simulating the maze using a number cube and to ask which cave one is more likely to end in.

- *How could we use a number cube to simulate walking through the maze and choosing paths at random to find an experimental probability?*

Help students see that rolling a 1 or 2 can represent choosing the upper path, a 3 or 4 the middle path, and a 5 or 6 the lower path.

Play a version of the game with the class. As students make their selections, demonstrate them at the board or overhead. To help students focus on the initial path choices, you may want to cover all but the first intersection until they have made their first choice.

You might show the diagram in Question C so that the work in Questions A and B will help them think about Question C.

Point out that Question E asks them to work backwards and create a game board to match the area model of probabilities given.

Have students work in groups of 3 or 4.

Materials

- Transparency 2.2A

Explore

As groups work, ask questions about what they are discovering.

- *Which cave seems to have the greater probability of the player entering it? What makes you think this?*
- *If you come to a fork that splits into three paths, what probability does each path have of being selected?*
- *Suppose your first choice is to take one of three paths, each of which is followed by a choice of two paths. What is the probability that you will take any given second path?*

Materials

- Number cubes
- Colored blocks
- Coins
- Large sheets of paper
- Markers

Have students share their experimental probabilities for each cave. Discuss reasons for variation in the data. Ask questions about other ways to make random choices at each split in the path. Pool the class experimental data and compare it with the theoretical data from the area analysis. Have students share their designs for Question E and determine whether they are correct. Ask what strategies they used.

Check for Understanding

For a further check on whether students understand how to find the probabilities of successive events, draw another maze for the class to analyze.

Materials
- Transparency 2.2B
- Student notebooks

ACE Assignment Guide for Problem 2.2

Differentiated Instruction
Solutions for All Learners

Core 4–7
Other *Connections* 15–22, *Extensions* 26; unassigned choices from previous problems

Adapted For suggestions about adapting ACE exercises, see the CMP *Special Needs Handbook*.
Connecting to Prior Units Exercise 21: *Data About Us*

Answers to Problem 2.2

A. Results will vary.

B. Answers may vary depending on the results in A. Combining all of the class data should bring the experimental probabilities close to the theoretical probabilities of $\frac{11}{18} \approx 61\%$ for Cave A and $\frac{7}{18} \approx 39\%$ for Cave B.

C. See diagrams in the Explore.

1. Miguel has recognized that each of the paths after the first split has a $\frac{1}{3}$ probability of being chosen. He has partitioned the square so that each of the three paths has the same probability.

2. See diagram and discussion in the Explore.
   $P(\text{A}) = \frac{11}{18}$ and $P(\text{B}) = \frac{7}{18}$.

D. If you combined the class's experimental data, their experimental probabilities should be close to the theoretical probabilities.

E. 1. Game screens will vary slightly, but should have a structure similar to the ones shown at right: There are three main paths. The top path splits into two, the middle path

does not split, and the bottom path splits into four. Example *c* below is a potential wrong answer (note that the bottom path splits into four paths that are not each equally likely).

Example a

Example b

Example c: a wrong game

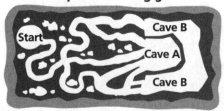

2. Cave A: $\frac{2}{3}$

$$\left(\tfrac{1}{3}\right)\left(\tfrac{1}{2}\right) + \left(\tfrac{1}{3}\right) + \left(\tfrac{1}{3}\right)\left(\tfrac{1}{4}\right) + \left(\tfrac{1}{3}\right)\left(\tfrac{1}{4}\right) =$$

$$\tfrac{1}{6} + \tfrac{1}{3} + \tfrac{1}{12} + \tfrac{1}{12} = \tfrac{2}{3}$$

Cave B: $\frac{1}{3}$

$$\left(\tfrac{1}{3}\right)\left(\tfrac{1}{2}\right) + \left(\tfrac{1}{3}\right)\left(\tfrac{1}{4}\right) + \left(\tfrac{1}{3}\right)\left(\tfrac{1}{4}\right) = \tfrac{1}{6} + \tfrac{1}{12} + \tfrac{1}{12} = \tfrac{1}{3}$$

Mathematical Goal

• Use an area model to analyze the theoretical probabilities for two-stage outcomes

This problem gives students another chance to analyze situations using an area model. This game involves two stages. An area model allows students to focus on one stage at a time.

Launch 2.3

Begin by telling the story of the game Brianna and Emmanuel are to play.

Suggested Question Ask students:

• *How would you arrange the marbles in the two containers so that you will have the greatest chance of choosing a green marble?*

Most students will suggest putting one green and one blue marble in each container. But there is another way to arrange the marbles to get a greater probability of choosing the green marble.

When students understand the game, have groups of three or four work on the problem. Each group will need two blocks, marbles, or other manipulatives in each of two colors and two identical opaque containers.

Let the class work in groups of two to four.

Explore 2.3

Students may struggle to find all the ways the four marbles can be arranged in two containers. Also, they may not see a relationship between this problem and other problems in this investigation. Thus they may not realize that an area model is a reasonable way to find the theoretical probability of drawing a green marble from each of the possible arrangements.

It is likely that many students will not initially realize that the probability of drawing a green marble when two blue marbles are in Container 1 and two green marbles are in Container 2 is equal to the probability of drawing a green marble when

two blue marbles are in Container 2 and two green marbles are in Container 1. There is no need to analyze both arrangements. Rather than pointing out that the containers are interchangeable and that these are equivalent situations, you may want to let students struggle with this idea, reach decisions about it within their groups, then clear up any misunderstanding during the summary.

Suggested Questions As groups explore the problem, ask questions to help them make sense of their work:

• *How do you know that you have considered all the possible ways to arrange the marbles in the containers?*

If a group is really struggling with finding all the arrangements, model another arrangement with them or ask them:

• *Could a container contain just one marble?*

• *Could we put all the marbles into one container?*

To help the students see that an area model might be useful, ask the following questions:

• *Once Brianna has put the marbles in the containers, what is the first choice that Emmanuel must make?* (He must select a container.)

• *What does Emmanuel do after he selects a container?* (He reaches in and, unless the container is empty, draws out a marble.)

• *Think about the two choices Emmanuel has to make. What do you think is the probability of him drawing a green marble in each of the arrangements? How might you show these two choices in your analysis?*

• *How can you use what you learned in the last problem about using an area model to help you analyze this problem?*

Going Further

If groups finish early, ask them to find the best arrangement if you have three marbles of each color.

Ask for all the ways the four marbles can be placed in the two containers. If students do not give all five arrangements (there are five if we consider GGB, B to be the same as B, GGB), say that you have another, and ask whether they can discover it. Putting all the marbles into one container is an arrangement students often miss.

Here are the five basic arrangements, not counting swapping Containers 1 and 2.

The associated theoretical probabilities of drawing a green marble from each arrangement are as follows:

Container 1	Container 2	P (Green)
BBGG	empty	$\frac{1}{4}$
BBG	G	$\frac{2}{3}$
BB	GG	$\frac{1}{2}$
B	GGB	$\frac{1}{3}$
BG	BG	$\frac{1}{2}$

Ask which arrangement will give Brianna and Emmanuel the best chance of winning. For each arrangement the groups suggest, have someone from that group illustrate on the board how they determined that it would give the friends the best chance of winning. If a particular group does not use an area analysis, ask another group to show how an area model could be used to analyze that arrangement. If groups have other strategies, give them a chance to offer these for class consideration.

You should have a different group present their area analysis to the class or use instructions from the class to draw the model and then interpret the model at the board.

Some students have trouble understanding the probability of drawing a green marble when all the marbles are placed in one container.

Suggested Questions You may want to work through this situation with the class.

- *Let's use an area model to represent putting all four marbles in one container. What is the first decision Emmanuel must make?* (He must select a container.)

- *How do we represent this with an area model?* (A square could be drawn to represent the total probability, and it could be divided into two equal parts to represent the choice between the two containers.)

- *After selecting a container, what must Emmanuel do to complete the game?* (Emmanuel must reach in and select a marble. If he chooses the empty container, when he reaches in he will get nothing.)

- *How can you represent this step with our area model?*

The region representing the container of four marbles (Container 1) must be divided into four equal parts, two for green and two for blue. The region for the other container needs no further division. The result is the diagram below.

Container 1 Container 2

green	
green	
blue	
blue	

- *Based on our area model, what is the probability of drawing a green marble with this arrangement? ($\frac{2}{8} = \frac{1}{4}$)*

- *What is the probability of drawing a blue marble? ($\frac{1}{4}$)*

- *What is the probability of drawing no marble? ($\frac{1}{2}$)*

- *Which arrangement gives the friends the worst chance of winning?*

Collect all ideas, again having students illustrate their analysis of each arrangement they suggest.

Going Further

You could pose the question from the Explore of arranging three marbles of each color in two identical containers.

2.3 Finding the Best Arrangement

Mathematical Goal

- Use an area model to analyze the theoretical probabilities for two-stage outcomes

Launch

Begin by telling the story of the game Brianna and Emmanuel are to play. Ask:

- *How would you arrange the marbles in the two containers so that you will have the greatest chance of choosing a green marble?*

When students understand the game, have groups of three or four work on the problem. Let the class work in groups of two to four.

Materials
- Transparency 2.3

Explore

As groups explore the problem, ask questions to help them make sense of their work.

- *How do you know that you have considered all the possible ways to arrange the marbles in the containers?*

If a group is really struggling with finding all the arrangements, model another arrangement with them or ask them:

- *Could a container contain just one marble?*
- *Could we put all the marbles into one container?*

Help students see that an area model might be useful.

- *Once Brianna has put the marbles in the containers, what is the first choice that Emmanuel must make?*
- *What does Emmanuel do after he selects a container?*
- *How can you use what you learned in the last problem about using an area model to help you analyze this problem?*

Going Further

If groups finish early, you can challenge them to find the best arrangement if you have three marbles of each color.

Materials
- Pairs of identical opaque containers
- Colored blocks or marbles

Summarize

Ask for all the ways the four marbles can be placed in the two containers. Ask which arrangement will give Brianna and Emmanuel the best chance of winning. For each arrangement the groups suggest, have someone from that group illustrate on the board how they determined that it would give the friends the best chance of winning. If a particular group does not use an area

Materials
- Student notebooks

continued on next page

analysis, ask another group to show how an area model could be used to analyze that arrangement. If groups have other strategies, give them a chance to offer these for class consideration.

● *Based on our area model, what is the probability of drawing a green marble with this arrangement? What is the probability of drawing a blue marble? What is the probability of drawing no marble? Which arrangement gives the friends the worst chance of winning?*

ACE Assignment Guide for Problem 2.3

Core 8–11
Other *Applications* 12; *Connections* 23, 24; *Extensions* 27, 28; unassigned choices from previous problems

Adapted For suggestions about adapting Exercise 23 and other ACE exercises, see the CMP *Special Needs Handbook*.

Answers to Problem 2.3

A–B. Note that the probabilities are given here for reference. The containers can be reversed, but the probabilities for the arrangements remain the same.

Container 1	Container 2	P (Green)
BBGG	empty	$\frac{1}{4}$
BBG	G	$\frac{2}{3}$
BB	GG	$\frac{1}{2}$
B	GGB	$\frac{1}{3}$
BG	BG	$\frac{1}{2}$

C. The arrangement of one green marble in one container and the three other marbles in the second container gives them the best chance of winning. The probability of drawing green from the arrangement of one green marble in one container and the three other marbles in the second container is $\frac{2}{3}$. When you use a square to analyze this option, the area for green is greater than in the other options. The arrangement of all four marbles in one container gives them the worst chance of winning. The probability of drawing a green marble with this arrangement is only $\frac{1}{4}$.

The student edition pages for this investigation begin on the next page.

STUDENT PAGE

Notes _____

_____

_____

_____

Investigation 2

Analyzing Situations Using an Area Model

Each turn in the games of chance in the last Investigation involved two actions. For example, in the spinner game, you spun the pointer twice and then determined the outcome. You determined the theoretical probabilities of these games using a variety of strategies.

In this Investigation, you will learn how to use an area model to analyze probability situations that involve more than one action on a turn. You can analyze games such as the Red and Blue game in Problem 1.2 using an **area model.**

Bucket 1 contains three marbles—one red and two greens. Bucket 2 contains four marbles—one red, one blue, one green, and one yellow.

Bucket 1

Bucket 2

- Draw a square on grid paper. Suppose the square has an area of 1 square unit. We use the square to represent a probability of 1.

Bucket 2

Bucket 1

Notes _____

_____

_____

_____

- The first bucket has three equally likely choices: red, green, and the other green. Divide the square into three sections with equal areas. The areas of the sections represent the probabilities of the three choices. Label the sections.

- For the second action of choosing a marble from Bucket 2, subdivide the diagram to represent the probabilities of the equally likely choices: red, blue, green, and yellow. Label these new Bucket 2 sections.

- Each subregion formed represents one of the outcomes: RR, RB, RG, RY, GR, GB, GG, and GY.

Bucket 2

	R	B	G	Y
R	RR	RB	RG	RY
G	GR	GB	GG	GY
G	GR	GB	GG	GY

Bucket 1

- The area of each subregion represents the probability for each outcome.

What is the probability of choosing an RR? RB? RG? RY? GR? GB? GG? GY? YY?

What is the probability of choosing a red from either bucket?

Notes _____

_____

_____

_____

A popular game at a school carnival is a spinner game called Making Purple. To play the game, a player spins the pointer of each spinner below once. Suppose a player gets red on one spinner and blue on the other spinner. The player wins, because red and blue together make purple.

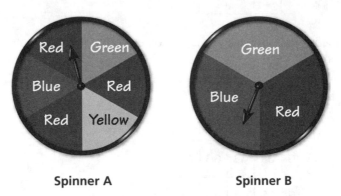

Spinner A   Spinner B

Notes _____

_____

_____

_____

A. Play the Making Purple game several times. Record the results of each turn. Based on your results, what is the experimental probability that a player will "make purple" on a turn?

B. Use an area model to determine the theoretical probability that a player will make purple on a turn.

C. How does the experimental probability of making purple compare with the theoretical probability of making purple?

D. The cost to play the game is $2. The winner gets $6 for making purple. Suppose 36 people play the game.

    1. How much money will the school take in from this game?

    2. How much money do you expect the school to pay out in prizes?

    3. How much profit do you expect the school to make from this game?

ACE Homework starts on page 27.

Notes _____

_____

_____

_____

Choosing Paths

Kenisha is designing a game involving paths through the woods that lead
to caves. Before the game is played the player chooses either Cave A or
Cave B. Next, the player starts at the beginning and chooses a path at
random at each fork. If the player lands in the cave that was chosen in the
beginning, he or she wins a prize.

Getting Ready for Problem 2.2

- Are you more likely to end in Cave A or in Cave B? Why?

The 18 students in Sarah's class design an experiment to find the likelihood
of ending in Cave A or in Cave B. For each trial, they trace the path
beginning at Start, and use a number cube to make the choice of direction
whenever there is a split in the path.

- Is this a good way to find the experimental probability of the game?
  Explain.

- Are there other ways to make choices at a split in the path? Explain.

24   What Do You Expect?

Notes _____

_____

_____

_____

A. Carry out the experiment to simulate the 18 students playing the game and note the cave where each student ends.

B. What is the experimental probability of landing in Cave A? Of landing in Cave B?

C. Miguel draws this diagram to help him find the theoretical probabilities of ending in Cave A or in Cave B.

Upper Path	
Middle Path	
Lower Path	

  1. Explain what Miguel has done so far. Does this look reasonable?

  2. Complete an area model to find the theoretical probabilities of ending in Cave A or Cave B. Show your work.

D. How are your experimental probabilities from Question A related to the theoretical probabilities?

E. Kenisha designs a new version of the game. It has a different arrangement of paths leading to Caves A and B. She makes the area model below to analyze the probabilities of ending in each cave.

  1. Create a path game that fits the model.

  2. Find the probability for each outcome.

ACE **Homework starts on page 27.**

Notes _____

_____

_____

_____

2.3 Finding the Best Arrangement

Brianna and Emmanuel are chosen from the studio audience of the Gee Whiz Everyone Wins! game show to play a game. While Emmanuel waits backstage, Brianna places two green marbles and two blue marbles in two identical containers in any arrangement she chooses.

After she places the marbles, Emmanuel returns. He chooses one of the containers at random. He then chooses a marble from that container without looking. If he chooses a green marble, the friends each win a prize. If he chooses a blue marble, or if the container he chooses is empty, the friends do not win anything.

Problem 2.3 Finding the Best Arrangement

A. List all the different ways Brianna can place the four marbles in the two containers.

B. For each arrangement, what is the probability that Emmanuel chooses a green marble?

C. Which arrangement will give Brianna and Emmanuel the greatest chance of winning? The least chance of winning? Explain.

ACE Homework starts on page 27.

Notes _____

_____

_____

_____

Applications

Connections

Extensions

Applications

1. Bonita and Deion are using the spinners from the Making Purple game in Problem 2.1. They take turns spinning. If the colors on the two spinners make purple, Deion scores. If they do not make purple, Bonita scores. For this to be a fair game, how many points should Deion score when the spinners make purple, and how many points should Bonita score when they do not make purple?

2. At the Flag Day Festival at Parker Middle School, there is a contest where a player chooses one block from each of two different bags. A player wins if he or she picks a red and a blue block. James makes the tree diagram below to find the probability of winning.

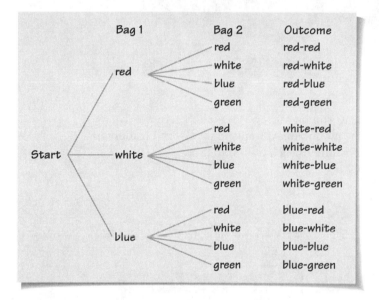

a. What blocks are in bag 1?

b. What blocks are in bag 2?

c. Draw an area model that represents this contest.

d. What is the probability of winning this contest?

For: Multiple-Choice Skills Practice
Web Code: ana-7254

Investigation 2 Analyzing Situations Using an Area Model   **27**

Notes _____

_____

_____

_____

3. There are two No-Cavity prize bins at a dentist's office. One bin has two hot-pink toothbrushes and three neon-yellow toothbrushes. The other bin has four packs of sugar-free gum, three grape and one strawberry. Kira has no cavities. The dentist tells her to close her eyes and choose a prize from each bin.

a. What is the probability that Kira will choose a neon-yellow toothbrush and a pack of sugar-free grape gum? Draw an area model to support your solution.

b. The dental assistant refills the bins after every patient. Suppose the next 100 patients have no cavities. How many times do you expect the patients to get the same prizes that Kira chose?

4. Al is about to ski his last run on Morey Mountain. There are five trails to the base of the mountain. Al wants to take a trail leading to the lodge. He can't remember which trail(s) to take.

Morey Mountain

Ski Lift   Lodge   Ski Shop

a. Design an experiment using a number cube to find the experimental probability of Al ending at the lodge. Conduct the experiment 20 times. If you do not have a number cube, write the numbers 1–6 on pieces of paper. Then select one from a hat.

Notes _____

_____

_____

_____

b. What is the experimental probability of Al ending at the lodge? At the lift? At the ski shop?

c. Find the theoretical probability of ending at the lodge, the lift, and the ski shop. Compare the experimental and theoretical probabilities. Do you have more confidence in the experimental or the theoretical probability? Why?

5. Kenisha changes the game in Problem 2.2 so it has the paths below.

a. Suppose a player chooses a path at random at each fork. What is the theoretical probability that he or she will end in Cave A? In Cave B? Show your work.

b. If you play this game 100 times, how many times do you expect to end in Cave A? In Cave B?

Notes _____

_____

_____

_____

6. Kenisha designs another version of the game in Problem 2.2. The new version has a different arrangement of paths leading into Caves A and B. She makes an area model to analyze the probabilities of landing in each cave.

For Kenisha's new version, what is the probability that a player will end in Cave A? In Cave B?

```
┌──────────┬──────────┐
│          │    B     │
│    A     ├──────────┤
│          │    A     │
├──────────┴──────────┤
│    A     │          │
├──────────┤    A     │
│    B     │          │
└──────────┴──────────┘
```

7. Multiple Choice Choose the map that the area model in Exercise 6 could represent.

A.

B.

C.

D.

Notes _____

_____

_____

_____

For Exercises 8–10, suppose a bag contains three orange marbles and two blue marbles. You are to choose a marble, return it to the bag, and then choose again.

8. Choose an appropriate method from those below for finding the possible outcomes. Describe how you would use your choice.

    a. make a tree diagram

    b. make a list

    c. use an area model

    d. make a table or chart

9. Suppose you do this experiment 50 times. Use the method you chose in Exercise 8 to predict the number of times you will choose two marbles of the same color.

10. Suppose this experiment is a two-person game in which one player scores if the marbles match, and the other player scores if they do not match. Suppose the two players play the game many times and total the points scored. Describe a scoring system that makes this a game in which each person has an equally likely chance of having the winning score.

Brianna (from Problem 2.3) is given each set of marbles to distribute between two containers. What arrangement gives Emmanuel the best chance of choosing a green marble?

11. three blue and two green marbles

12. two blue and three green marbles

Notes _____

_____

_____

_____

Connections

13. In a survey, 100 seniors at a high school were asked these questions:

- Do you favor a rule that allows only seniors to drive to school?
- Do you drive to school?

Homework Help Online
PHSchool.com
For: Help with Exercise 13
Web Code: ane-7213

Driving Survey

	Drives to School	Does Not Drive to School	Row Totals
Favors Rule	40	30	70
Opposes Rule	20	10	30
Total	60	40	100

a. Based on this survey, what is the probability that a senior chosen at random favors the rule?

b. What is the probability that a senior chosen at random drives to school and favors the rule?

c. What is the probability that a senior chosen at random drives to school or opposes the rule?

d. Are the results of this survey a good indicator of how all the students at the high school feel about the driving rule? Explain.

Notes _____

_____

_____

_____

14. Marni and Ira are playing a game with this square spinner. A game is 10 turns. Each turn is 2 spins. The numbers for the 2 spins are added. Marni scores 1 point for a sum that is negative, and Ira scores 1 point for a sum that is positive. After 10 turns, each player totals their points. The one with more points wins.

    a. List all of the possible outcomes.

    b. Are Marni and Ira equally likely to win?

Megan is designing a computer game called *Treasure Hunt*. The computer chooses a square at random on the grid at the right, and then hides a treasure in the room containing that square. For Exercises 15–19, use the grid to find the probability that the computer will hide the treasure in each room.

15. Library

16. Den

17. Dining hall

18. Great hall

19. Front hall

20. Multiple Choice Megan enlarges the floor plan in the game grid above by a scale factor of 2. How does this affect the probabilities that the treasure is in each room?

    F. They are unchanged.

    G. They are $\frac{1}{2}$ the original probability.

    H. They are twice the original.

    J. They are four times the original.

Notes _____

_____

_____

_____

21. Carlos is also designing a *Treasure Hunt* game. He keeps track of the number of times the computer hides the treasure in each room. Here is a line plot of his results.

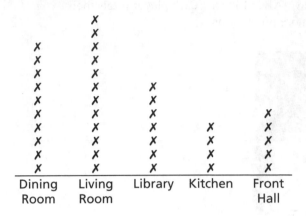

Design a floor plan that could give this data. State the area of each room on your floor plan.

22. Fergus designs a dartboard for a school carnival. His design is shown below. He must decide how much to charge a player and how much to pay out for a win. To do this, he needs to know the probabilities of landing in sections marked A and B. Assume the darts land at random on the dartboard.

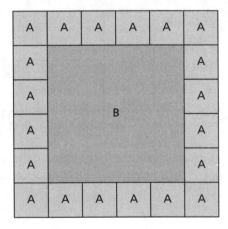

a. What is the probability of landing in a section marked A?

b. What is the probability of landing in a section marked B?

Notes _____

_____

_____

_____

23. Fergus designs two more dartboards for the school carnival.

Dartboard 1

Dartboard 2

a. What is the probability of landing in sections marked A on Dartboard 1? On Dartboard 2? Explain.

b. A player pays $1 to play and wins $2 if the dart lands in sections marked B. If the dart lands in sections marked A, the player wins no money.

  i. How much money will the player expect to make (or lose) after 36 turns using Dartboard 1? Using Dartboard 2? Explain.

  ii. How much money will the carnival expect to make (or lose) after 36 turns using Dartboard 1? Using Dartboard 2?

c. Can the carnival expect to make a profit on this game with either board? Explain.

24. a. If you roll one number cube two times, what is the probability of getting a factor of 5 both times?

b. Suppose you roll two different number cubes. What is the probability of getting a factor of 5 on both cubes?

c. How do your answers to parts (a) and (b) compare? Explain why the answers have this relationship.

Investigation 2 Analyzing Situations Using an Area Model   **35**

Notes _____

_____

_____

_____

Extensions

25. Suppose you play a game using the two spinners below. You get two spins. You may spin each spinner once, or you may spin one of the spinners twice. If you get a red on one spin and a blue on the other spin (the order makes no difference), you win. To have the greatest chance of winning, should you spin Spinner A twice, spin Spinner B twice, or spin each spinner once? Explain.

Spinner A   Spinner B

26. Suppose Brianna (from Problem 2.3) is given two green marbles, two blue marbles, and three buckets. How can she put the marbles in the three buckets to have the best chance of choosing a green marble?

27. Della is chosen as a contestant on a game show. The host gives her two red marbles, two green marbles, and two yellow marbles.

Della will put the marbles into two identical cans in any way she chooses. The host will then rearrange the cans, leaving the marbles as Della placed them. Della will then select a can and choose a marble. If she chooses a red marble, she wins a prize.

How should Della arrange the marbles so she has the best chance of choosing a red marble?

28. Make up your own marbles and buckets problem. Find the solution.

Mathematical Reflections 2

In this investigation, you analyzed probabilities of two-stage events by dividing the area of a square. The following questions will help you summarize what you have learned.

Think about your answers to these questions. Discuss your ideas with other students and your teacher. Then write a summary of your findings in your notebook.

1. Describe three or four probability situations that involve two actions. Describe the outcomes for these situations.

2. Describe how you can use an area model to determine the probability of a situation that involves two actions.

STUDENT PAGE

Notes _____

_____

_____

_____

Investigation

ACE Assignment Choices

Differentiated Instruction
Solutions for All Learners

Problem 2.1

Core 2, 3
Other *Applications* 1; *Connections* 13, 14; *Extensions* 25

Problem 2.2

Core 4–7
Other *Connections* 15–22, *Extensions* 26; unassigned choices from previous problems

Problem 2.3

Core 8–11
Other *Applications* 12; *Connections* 23, 24; *Extensions* 27, 28; unassigned choices from previous problems

Adapted For suggestions about adapting Exercise 23 and other ACE exercises, see the CMP *Special Needs Handbook*.
Connecting to Prior Units 13, 21: *Data About Us*; 14: *Accentuate the Negative*

Applications

1. Deion should score 7 (or 14) points when the spinners make purple and Bonita should score 2 (or 4, if Deion scores 14) points when the spinners do not make purple. This is because Deion has a $\frac{4}{18} = \frac{2}{9}$ chance of making purple and Bonita has a $\frac{14}{18} = \frac{7}{9}$ chance of not making purple. For example, if the spinners were spun 54 times, Deion would get purple 12 times, scoring 12×7 points in the long run, which equals 84 points; Bonita would not get purple 42 times, scoring 42×2 points in the long run, which equals 84 points.

2. **a.** one red, one white, and one blue
   b. one red, one white, one blue and one green

c.

	Red	White	Blue	Green
Red			▓	
White				
Blue	▓			

d. $\frac{2}{12} = \frac{1}{6}$

3. **a.**

Packs of gum

	3 grape			1 strawberry

(Toothbrushes: 3 neon-yellow, 2 hot-pink)

Kira has a $\frac{9}{20}$ probability of drawing a neon-yellow toothbrush and a pack of grape gum.

b. Of 100 patients, you could expect about 45 $(\frac{9}{20} \times 100)$ to draw the same prizes Kira chose.

4. **a.** Possible answer: At each fork that splits into two trails, if even is rolled, go to the right, and if odd is rolled, go to the left. At the fork that splits into three trails, if you roll a 1 or 2, choose the leftmost path; a 3 or 4, choose the middle path; and a 5 or 6 choose the rightmost path.

b. Answers will vary.

c.

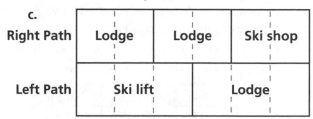

Right Path	Lodge	Lodge	Ski shop
Left Path	Ski lift		Lodge

For large numbers of experiments, the probabilities should be close to the theoretical probability of $\frac{7}{12}$ for the lodge, $\frac{1}{4}$ for the lift, $\frac{1}{6}$ for the ski shop.

5. a. Cave A: $\frac{7}{12}$; $\frac{1}{6} + \frac{1}{6} + \frac{1}{8} + \frac{1}{8} = \frac{7}{12} \approx 58\%$

Cave B: $\frac{5}{12}$; $\frac{1}{6} + \frac{1}{4} = \frac{5}{12} \approx 42\%$

A square can be divided to show the probability of a player ending in each cave, as shown below.

b. If you played the game 100 times, you could expect to end in

Cave A $100 \times \frac{7}{12} =$ about 58 times and in

Cave B $100 \times \frac{5}{12} =$ about 42 times.

6. Cave A: $\frac{3}{4}$ Cave B: $\frac{1}{4}$

$\frac{1}{4} + \frac{1}{8} + \frac{1}{8} + \frac{1}{4} = \frac{3}{4}$ $\frac{1}{8} + \frac{1}{8} = \frac{1}{4}$

7. B

8. Any of the methods could be used, although some might be easier to use than others.

a. To use a tree diagram, five branches would represent the first draw. From each of these, another five branches would represent the second draw. This would result in 25 different outcomes.

b. To use a list, you have to be careful to distinguish between the different orange and blue marbles (for example, by using symbols such as O1, O2, O3, B1, B2). You would list O1 with each of the other possibilities, and then O2 with each of the other possibilities, and so on.

c. To use an area model, you could divide a square into five rows to represent the first draw. Then, divide each row into five parts to represent the second draw.

d. A chart would resemble an area model, with five rows and five columns, as shown here:

	O	O	O	B	B
O	OO	OO	OO	OB	OB
O	OO	OO	OO	OB	OB
O	OO	OO	OO	OB	OB
B	BO	BO	BO	BB	BB
B	BO	BO	BO	BB	BB

9. Of the 25 possible outcomes, 13 represent marbles of the same color, so you could expect to draw two marbles of the same color, $\frac{13}{25}$ or 26 out of 50 times.

10. Possible answer: Award 12 points for a match; 13 points for a no-match.

11. The best arrangement is one green marble in one container and the remaining marbles in the other container. A square can be divided to show that the probability of drawing green is $\frac{5}{8}$.

12. The best arrangement is one green marble in one container and the remaining marbles in the other container. The probability of choosing green is $\frac{3}{4}$.

Connections

13. a. $\frac{70}{100}$ or 70%

b. $\frac{40}{100}$ or 40%

c. Of the 100 seniors surveyed, 60 drive to school. Of those who don't drive to school, 10 oppose the rule. This is a total of 70, so the probability is $\frac{70}{100}$. (Note: Adding the total number of seniors who drive to school (60) to the total number who oppose the rule (30) is incorrect because it double counts those who drive to school and oppose the rule.) Another way to do this problem is to determine who is not counted, seniors who do not drive to school and who favor the rule, for a total of 30, which leaves 70.

d. One problem with this survey is that it polled only seniors. Because the question concerns a rule that would allow only seniors to drive, many of the other students in the lower grades might oppose it. Thus this survey is probably not a good indicator of the opinions of the entire student body.

14. a.

		Second Spin			
		−1	2	3	−4
First Spin	**−1**	−2	1	2	−5
	2	1	4	5	−2
	3	2	5	6	−1
	−4	−5	−2	−1	−8

b. Yes, it is a fair game because positive and negative sums are equally likely ($\frac{8}{16}$).

15. $\frac{15}{100}$ **16.** $\frac{6}{100}$ **17.** $\frac{28}{100}$

18. $\frac{30}{100}$ **19.** $\frac{21}{100}$ **20.** F

21. Drawings will vary. According to the data, Rich played the game 38 times, and the experimental probabilities that the treasure will be in each room are as follows:

$P(\text{dining room}) = \frac{10}{38} \approx 0.26$

$P(\text{living room}) = \frac{12}{38} \approx 0.32$

$P(\text{library}) = \frac{7}{38} \approx 0.18$

$P(\text{kitchen}) = \frac{4}{38} \approx 0.11$

$P(\text{front hall}) = \frac{5}{38} \approx 0.13$

On a 10 by 10 grid, the dining room should occupy about 26 squares, the living room about 32 squares, the library about 18 squares, the kitchen about 11 squares, and the front hall about 13 squares.

22. a. $\frac{20}{36}$ or $\frac{5}{9}$ **b.** $\frac{4}{9}$

23. a. $P(\text{landing on A for Dartboard 1}) = \frac{18}{36}$;

$P(\text{landing on A for Dartboard 2}) = \frac{19}{36}$.

Each dartboard can be divided up into 36 equal pieces that are the size of the smallest square piece on each board.

b. i. For each dartboard a person pays $36 dollars to play 36 times.

For Dartboard 1: A person would make $0 since the probability of landing on B is $\frac{18}{36}$ and $2(18) - \$36 = \$0$

For Dartboard 2: A person would lose $2 since the probability of landing on B is $\frac{17}{36}$ or 17 out of 36 times and $2(17) - \$36 = -\$2$.

ii. The carnival would make $0 from Dartboard 1 and $2 from Dartboard 2.

c. Assuming the darts land at random, the carnival can expect to make a profit of $2 for each 36 plays or 5.6 cents per play on this game if players choose Dartboard 2. The carnival can expect to break even on Dartboard 1.

24. a. The factors of 5 are 5 and 1, so there is a $\frac{1}{3}$ chance on each roll of getting a factor of 5.

The probability of getting a factor of 5 on two consecutive rolls is $\frac{1}{9}$. (Note: Students may list all possible combinations, draw an area model, or if they see the connection to multiplying fractions, compute $\frac{1}{3} \times \frac{1}{3} = \frac{1}{9}$.)

b. $\frac{4}{36}$ or $\frac{1}{9}$

c. The answers are the same; rolling the same number cube a second time is equivalent to rolling a second number cube. Each roll of a number cube is independent of other rolls.

Extensions

25. One way to solve this is to make tables, as below. Within each table, each cell represents an equally likely outcome.

	Spinner A			
Spinner A		Green	Blue	Red	Yellow
Green				
Blue			■	
Red		■		
Yellow				

	Spinner B		
Spinner B		Green	Red	Blue
Green				■
Red				■
Blue			■	

	Spinner B		
Spinner A		Green	Red	Blue
Green				
Blue			■	
Yellow				
Red				■

The greatest chance of winning is in spinning spinner B twice. Possible explanation: The charts show that each way to spin the spinners results in two red-blue pairs; the way with the fewest possible outcomes is the best choice.

26. The best arrangement is to put one green marble in the first container, one green in the second container, and the two blue marbles in the other container. The probability of choosing green is $\frac{2}{3}$.

27. Della should put one red marble in one can and the remaining marbles in the other can. This will give her a $\frac{6}{10}$ probability of winning.

28. Answers will vary.

Possible Answers to Mathematical Reflections

1. Students will probably describe some of the situations from this investigation that involved two actions, such as a player choosing paths in the Choosing Paths Game. In this case, the outcomes are: Choosing to go left at the first intersection, then left at the second intersection; choosing to go left at the first intersection, then right at the second intersection, etc.

During class discussion of this question, ask students to think of other situations.

For example, suppose you have three T-shirts: one red, one blue, and one green. You also have four baseball caps: one red and blue, one green and yellow, one red and yellow, and one blue and white. Suppose you first choose a T-shirt at random. Then, you choose a cap at random from those that contain a color that matches the shirt. What is the probability that you will choose each combination with the matching colors?

There are five outcomes. The outcomes and probabilities are described in Question 2.

Another situation is choosing to carry or not to carry an umbrella after listening to the weather forecast.

2. A square area model is appropriate when there are two or more actions in a situation because you can show the different actions. The area of a square represents 1.

The example of selecting a shirt and then a cap from Question 1 is used to show how the area model can be used to determine the probability of selecting a shirt and hat that match. You can use a different example or modify this example.

First, you divide a square into three equal parts to represent the three shirt choices. Next, you need to determine the cap choices for each shirt. For each red shirt, there are two caps (red/blue and red/yellow); for the blue shirt, there are two caps (red/blue and blue/white). Each of these regions is divided in half. The green shirt corresponds to only one cap (green/yellow), so that region is not subdivided. The probability of choosing each cap can be found by adding its fractional areas. The red/blue cap has a probability of $\frac{1}{6} + \frac{1}{6} = \frac{1}{3}$, the red/yellow and blue/white caps each have a probability of $\frac{1}{6}$, and the green/yellow cap has a probability of $\frac{1}{3}$.

red shirt	red/blue cap	red/yellow cap
blue shirt	red/blue cap	blue/white cap
green shirt	green/yellow cap	

Investigation 3 — Expected Value

Mathematical and Problem-Solving Goals

- Understand the difference between the probability of an outcome and the long-term average of many trials in a situation with a payoff
- Determine the expected value in a probability situation
- Use probability to make decisions

Students continue to use an area model to find theoretical probabilities, but now they will determine the "long-term average" in chance situations. If a probability situation has some payoff associated with it, then expected value is the average payoff over many trials. Another way to say this is over the long run.

Summary of Problems

Problem 3.1 One-and-One Free-Throws

Students investigate two-stage outcomes in the context of a one-and-one free-throw situation. After determining experimental probabilities that the player will get a score of 0, 1, or 2, students find the theoretical probability by using an area model.

Problem 3.2 Finding Expected Value

Students determine the long-term average (expected value) for the one-and-one free-throw situation in the previous problem.

Problem 3.3 Choosing Pay Plans

Students use expected value to make decisions in a variety of different probability settings.

	Suggested Pacing	Materials for Students	Materials for Teachers	ACE Assignments
All	5 days	Hundredths grids (optional; blackline masters provided in the Labsheet section of TE)	Transparencies 3.1 and 3.2 (optional); transparency markers	
3.1	$1\frac{1}{2}$ days	Labsheet 3.1 (1 per pair); bobby pins or paper clips (for spinners, 1 per pair), colored blocks; ten-sided number cubes (optional)	Transparency 3.1 (optional)	1–3,10–15
3.2	$1\frac{1}{2}$ days	Labsheet 3.2 (optional; 1 per pair)	Transparency 3.2 (optional); transparency of Labsheet 3.2	4–7,16–19, 23–26, 28
3.3	$1\frac{1}{2}$ days	Large sheets of paper and markers (optional; 1 per pair)		8, 9, 20–22, 27
MR	$\frac{1}{2}$ day			

Mathematical Goals

- Understand the difference between the probability of an outcome and the long-term average of many trials in a situation with a payoff

- Determine the expected value in a probability situation

- Use probability to make decisions

In this problem the two-stage outcome is a one-and-one free-throw situation. A player with a 60% free-throw average goes for a one-and-one. That is, the player takes the first free throw and then either takes a second free throw (if the first one was made) or does not get a second chance (if the first free throw was missed).

Launch 3.1

Read the story of Nishi's basketball game, or personalize a similar story using teams and players that would be of interest to your class. Make sure everyone understands what free-throw and one-and-one situations are. Students who are not interested in basketball may need the one-and-one explained to them.

Suggested Questions Pose the questions in the Getting Ready for the students to discuss.

- *What are the possible numbers of points that Nishi could score in a one-and-one situation?* (0 points, 1 point, or 2 points)

- *Explain how each of these can happen.* (She will score 0 points if she misses the first basket, 1 point if she makes the first basket but misses the second, and 2 points if she makes both baskets.)

Pose Question A to the whole class:

- *Which score do you think is most likely to happen? Why?*

The intention of Question A is for students to express their ideas, not to finalize an argument. You could have students vote on which result they think is most likely. Most will guess that Nishi is most likely to score 1 point and the game will end in a tie.

- *How might you figure out what is most likely to happen?*

- *How could you simulate the situation to generate experimental data about the likelihood of each result?*

Each plan for simulating the situation must account for the following:

- a miss

- a hit followed by a miss

- a hit followed by a hit

This discussion should raise the question of how a simulation will handle the fact that getting a second try depends on whether the first attempt is made. Remind students that when they analyzed the Choosing Paths game, they simulated playing the game by using number cubes, spinners, coins, or colored blocks to generate random decisions about which path to take at each fork in the maze.

Suggested Questions Ask:

- *Could we use any of these methods to simulate Nishi's free-throw average of 60%?*

Here are three of the ways students might simulate this situation:

- Spin a spinner with two sections that represent the probability of making or missing the basket. One section has a 216° (60% of 360°) central angle for a hit. The other section has a 144° (40% of 360°) central angle for a miss. If the first spin lands in the hit section, the spinner is spun a second time. If the first spin lands in the miss section, the simulation is over.

- Roll a ten-sided number cube, letting 1, 2, 3, 4, 5, and 6 represent making the basket and 7, 8, 9, 10 (or 0) represent missing the basket. The number cube is rolled a second time only if the first roll lands on 1, 2, 3, 4, 5, or 6.

- Choose a colored block from a container holding ten blocks, six of one color to represent making the basket and four of another color to represent missing the basket. If the first block chosen is of the color representing making the basket, it is returned to the container and a second block is chosen.

To help students choose a method or methods, demonstrate how to simulate a one-and-one free-throw situation using several of the class's suggestions.

Tell the class about the spinners on Labsheet 3.1. (Two spinners are on each labsheet; simply cut the labsheet in half.)

Demonstrate on the overhead how to use the spinner. Demonstrate trials that end with one spin (or toss or choice) and trials that require two spins. The number of spins in a trial depends on whether the first spin represented making the basket or missing it. Show students what data they need to record and how to record it. The score from each trial is what is of interest. The data collected will be the number of times the simulation results in scores of 0 points, 1 point, and 2 points.

Take this opportunity to remind students about two important ideas: (1) the probability of an outcome not happening is 1 minus the probability of it happening, and (2) the probability of making or missing on the second attempt (assuming there *is* a second attempt) is still 60%.

Suggested Questions Ask:

- *When Nishi goes to the line for her first attempt, what is the probability that she will make the basket?* (60%)

- *What is the probability that she will miss the basket?* (40%)

- *If she makes the first basket, what is the probability that she will make the second basket?* (60%)

Some students may argue that the fact that Nishi made the first basket must be accounted for by re-computing the probability. Point out that the probability is based on a large number of trials and is affected very little by a single throw. Nishi still has a 60% free-throw average.

Let students work in pairs to conduct the experiment with whatever simulation methods they choose and to address the remaining parts of the problem.

As you circulate, check that each pair has a reasonable simulation method and understands how to collect the data. Make sure students are gathering data that accurately represents the situation. Each pair's results will contribute to the experimental probability of the class's combined data set, so all should be appropriate.

Ask pairs questions about what patterns are occurring in the data. In particular, ask them to think about how the second attempt is affected by, or how it depends on, what happens on the first basket.

Some students may need help with the area model. On the first throw the area of the square is separated into two parts to represent 60% and 40%. The area that represents 40% of the square represents a score of 0. On the second throw, only the area that represents 60% is further subdivided to represent 40% and 60%. (See the discussion and illustrations in the Summarize section.) For Question E, have students use an area model to be more specific in their answer.

Have the class combine all their data and find an overall experimental probability.

Ask two or three pairs to explain how they found their theoretical probabilities. The following is one way to use a 10 by 10 grid to make an area model of the situation and to assign theoretical probabilities. You may want to use a transparent 10 by 10 grid to show a couple of models.

Nishi's first attempt has two possible outcomes, either making the basket or missing the basket. The probability of making the basket is 60%, or $\frac{60}{100}$. The probability of missing the basket is 40%, or $\frac{40}{100}$. The grid is shaded to represent these probabilities.

Nishi will make her second attempt 60% of the times that she makes her first attempt, or an overall total of 0.6 × 0.6 = 0.36, or 36% of the time. She will miss her second attempt 40% of the time that she makes her first basket, or an overall total of 0.4 × 0.6 = 0.24, or 24% of the time. The grid below is shaded to show these probabilities.

Misses the first attempt

Makes both attempts **Makes the first attempt, misses the second**

The grid analysis helps students see that multiplying 0.60 × 0.60 and getting 0.36 is a numerical way to find the percent of the area allotted to receiving 2 points. It is also helpful to reiterate that we need to find 60% of 60% to represent the probability of Nishi receiving 2 points. Some students might observe that the analysis using the area model is analogous to a model for multiplying fractions:

P(a score of 2) = 60% × 60% = 36% and

P(a score of 2) = $\frac{6}{10} \times \frac{6}{10} = \frac{36}{100}$

P(a score of 1) = 60% × 40% = 24% and

P(a score of 1) = $\frac{6}{10} \times \frac{4}{10} = \frac{24}{100}$

P(a score of 0) = 40%

Help students compare the class's experimental probabilities to the theoretical probabilities. In most classrooms, these will be close as the only possibilities are 0 points, 1 point, and 2 points, and the class data will contain many trials. However, as the probability of 0 points and 2 points are similar, the class data may not distinguish between them.

Going Further

When students finish discussing the problem, give pairs a few minutes to consider the following question.

- *Suppose Nishi is in a two-attempt free-throw situation. This means that she will get a second try even if she misses the first one. What is the theoretical probability that Nishi will score 0 points? That she will score 1 point? That she will score 2 points?*

The challenge is to determine how the area model would change if Nishi automatically gets a second try. That is, she gets to take two free-throw attempts.

As a class, discuss how the grid should be divided to represent this situation. Make sure students see that, in this area model, two sections are marked 1 point. Nishi can get 1 point in two ways: by making the first try and missing the second, or by missing the first try and making the second.

One way to keep track of the computations in finding the probabilities is to use an area model. The analysis for a player with a 60% average in a two-attempt free-throw situation and the expected value or long-term average looks as follows:

Misses the first attempt, makes the second   **Misses both attempts**

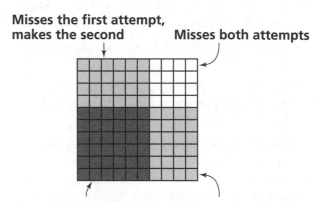

Makes both attempts   **Makes the first attempt, misses the second**

Note that expected value is not discussed until the next problem.

Suggested Question You could launch the next problem by asking:

- *If Nishi's free throw does not change, what is her average number of points per each one-and-one situation?*

One-and-One Free-Throws

Mathematical Goals

- Understand the difference between the probability of an outcome and the long-term average of many trials in a situation with a payoff
- Determine the expected value in a probability situation
- Use probability to make decisions

Launch

Tell the story of Nishi's basketball game. Make sure everyone understands what free-throw and one-and-one situations are. Pose the questions in the Getting Ready for the students to discuss.

- *What are the possible numbers of points that Nishi could score in a one-and-one situation?*
- *Explain how each of these can happen.*

Pose Question A to the whole class:

- *Which score do you think is most likely to happen? Why?*
- *How might you figure out what is most likely to happen?*
- *How could you simulate the situation to generate experimental data about the likelihood of each result?*

This discussion should raise the question of how a simulation will handle the fact that getting a second try depends on whether the first attempt is made. Remind students that when they analyzed the Choosing Paths game, they simulated playing the game by using number cubes, spinners, coins, or colored blocks to generate random decisions about which path to take at each fork in the maze.

Tell the class about the spinners on Labsheet 3.1. (Two spinners are on each labsheet; simply cut the labsheet in half.)

Demonstrate on the overhead how to use the spinner.

Let students work in pairs to conduct the experiment with whatever simulation methods they choose and to address the remaining parts of the problem.

Materials

- Transparency 3.1

Explore

Check that each pair has a reasonable simulation method and understands how to collect the data. Make sure students are gathering data that accurately represents the situation.

Some students may need help with the area model.

Materials

- Labsheet 3.1
- Bobby pins or paper clips
- Colored blocks
- 10-sided number cubes

Summarize

Have the class combine all their data and find an overall experimental probability. Ask two or three pairs to explain how they found their theoretical probabilities. Be sure the class understands the area model. Help students compare the class's experimental probabilities with the theoretical probabilities. In most classrooms, these will be close as the only possibilities are 0 points, 1 point, and 2 points, and the class data will contain many trials. However, as the probability of 0 points and 2 points are similar, the class data may not distinguish between them.

Materials
- Student notebooks

ACE Assignment Guide for Problem 3.1

Core 1–3, 15
Other *Connections* 10–14

Adapted For suggestions about adapting Exercise 3 and other ACE exercises, see the CMP *Special Needs Handbook*.
Connecting to Prior Units 12–15: *Bits and Pieces III*

Answers to Problem 3.1

A. Answers will vary. Many students will guess that 1 point is the most likely result.

B. Answers will vary. One possible result from a group is: 0 points (seven times); 1 point (five times); and 2 points (eight times).

C. Answers will vary. For the results reported above, experimental probability is:

$P(0 \text{ points}) = \frac{7}{20} = 35\%,$

$P(1 \text{ point}) = \frac{5}{20} = 25\%,$ and

$P(2 \text{ points}) = \frac{8}{20} = 40\%.$

D. Possible area model:

$P(0 \text{ points}) = \frac{40}{100} = 40\%,$

$P(1 \text{ point}) = \frac{24}{100} = 24\%,$

$P(2 \text{ points}) = \frac{36}{100} = 36\%$

Answers will vary. The experimental probabilities in Question C are close to the theoretical probabilities. The experiment had slightly more 2's and 1's than expected and slightly fewer 0's. As the number of trials was small, this is not surprising.

E. Her probabilities for getting 0 and 1 point will decrease. However, the probability for getting 2 points will increase. She will get 0 points 30% of the time, 1 point 21% of the time, and 2 points 49% of the time.

F. The diagram shows that Nishi has a 36% chance of scoring two points. So, after 100 situations, she will score about 36 points. After 200 situations, she will score about 72 points.

Finding Expected Value

Mathematical Goal

• Determine the expected value in a probability situation

In this problem, students consider expected value, or long-term average. If a player with a 60% free-throw average goes to the line for a one-and-one situation throughout the season, what is his or her average for each one-and-one free-throw situation?

Math Background

For background on expected value, see page 7.

Launch 3.2

Question A of this problem can be done as a whole-class activity or in pairs.

Suggested Questions If you do Questions A and B as a whole class, ask students to explore the expected values for other percents.

• *In 100 one-and-one free-throw situations, how many times could Nishi expect to get a score of 0?* (40)

• *A score of 1?* (24) *A score of 2?* (36)

• *What is the total number of points Nishi could expect to score in 100 trips to the free-throw line?* (For the 40 times that Nishi expects a score of 0 points, she would accumulate 0 points. For the 24 times that she expects a score of 1 point, she would accumulate 24 points. For the 36 times that she expects a score of 2 points, she would accumulate 72 points. This is an overall total of $0 + 24 + 72 = 96$ points.)

Here is a useful way to organize this work:

0 points × 40 = 0
1 point × 24 = 24
2 points × 36 = 72
total = 96

• *What would her average score per trip be?* ($96 \div 100 = 0.96$ point/trip)

Point out that this is a little bit less than 1 point per trip. Then, explain the following:

• *In Problem 3.1, the majority of you guessed that Nishi's most likely score on a trip to the line would be 1 point—you were giving the right answer, but to the wrong question! Her long-term average is about 1 point, but the most likely result of a player with a 60% average for a particular one-and-one free-throw attempt is 0 points.*

• *The average number of points per trip is the expected value. We usually find the expected value over many trips, or many trials. We can think of the expected value as a long-term average.*

• *We computed the expected value for Nishi using 100 one-and-one free-throw attempts. Would it make a difference if we used 200 trials instead of 100 to compute the expected value? Why or why not?*

You may want to demonstrate that it does not make a difference or ask the class to use a different number:

0 points × 80 = 0
1 point × 48 = 48
2 points × 72 = 144
total = 192

Nishi's average score per trip is still
$192 \div 200 = 0.96$ point/trip.

Questions B and C can be assigned for students to work in pairs.

Explore 3.2

Allow ample time for students to complete Questions B and C in class or individually at home. Labsheet 3.2 may help. Students need to work through a second example, in addition to the player with a 60% average, before they proceed on their own.

Summarize 3.2

Suggested Questions Review the answers in class.

• *What is the average number of points per trip that a player with a 60% average can expect?* (0.96)

- *A player with a 20% average?* (0.24)

- *A player with a 40% average?* (0.56)

- *A player with an 80% average?* (1.44)

- *How did you find your answers?*

If you did not go over the method for finding expected value with the whole class in Question A, do it now. Ask for strategies from the class.

Suggested Questions Ask the class:

- *What patterns did you observe in the table?*

Here are some patterns students have noticed:

- The probability of 0 points decreases as the player's average increases.

- The probability of 1 point increases and then decreases as the player's average increases.

- The probability of 2 points increases as the player's average increases.

- The probability of 2 points is always a square number.

- The expected value increases as the player's average increases.

Suggested Questions

- *What score is a player with a 50% average most likely to get?* (Half of the time, a player with a 50% average will miss. A player with a 50% average would most likely score 0 points.)

- *What can you tell about the expected value for a player with a 50% average from the information in your table?* (Since a player with a 40% average has an expected value of 0.56 points per trip and a player with a 60% average has an expected value of 0.96 points per trip, a player with a 50% average will have an expected value between 0.56 and 0.96 of a point per trip.)

- *Compute the expected value for a player with a 50% average, and tell me how you did it. Does your answer fit the table?* (It is 0.75.)

The analysis using 10 by 10 grids is quite efficient. However, some students may have begun to multiply probabilities to analyze such situations.

- *What is the free-throw average for a player whose expected value is exactly 1?* (From the graph in Question C, it is approximately 62%. But, the change is not linear. Connect the points with a curved line.)

Suggested Questions You can ask other questions that require students to use the graph.

- *What is the expected value for a player with a 75% free-throw average?*

- *Is the relationship linear? Explain.*

Going Further

Students can also calculate the expected value for various players in a two-attempt free-throw situation in which getting a second basket does not depend on making the first basket. You might ask students to calculate the difference between this expected value and the one for a one-and-one situation for players with 0%, 10%, . . . 100% averages.

3.2 Finding Expected Value

Mathematical Goal

- Determine the expected value in a probability situation

Launch

Question A of this problem can be done as a whole-class activity or in pairs.

- *In 100 one-and-one free-throw situations, how many times could Nishi expect to get a score of 0? A score of 1? A score of 2?*
- *What is the total number of points Nishi could expect to score in 100 trips to the free-throw line?*
- *What would her average score per trip be?*

In Problem 3.1, students predicted the most likely outcome. Here, they determine the average outcome.

- *The average number of points per trip is the* expected value. *We usually find the expected value, or long-term average, over many trials.*

Questions B and C can be assigned for students to work in pairs.

Materials
- Transparency 3.2
- Transparency of Labsheet 3.2

Vocabulary
- Expected value

Explore

Allow ample time for students to complete Questions B and C in class or individually at home. Labsheet 3.2 may help. Students need to work through a second example, in addition to that of the player with a 60% average, before they proceed on their own.

Materials
- Labsheet 3.2

Summarize

Review the answers in class.

- *What is the average number of points per trip that a player with a 60% average can expect? A player with a 20% average? A player with a 40% average? A player with an 80% average?*
- *How did you find your answers?*

If you did not go over the method for finding expected value with the whole class in Question A, do it now. Ask for strategies from the class.

Discuss any patterns students notice in the table.

- *What score is a player with a 50% average most likely to get?*
- *What can you tell about the expected value for a player with a 50% average from the information in your table?*

The analysis using 10 by 10 grids is quite efficient. However, some students may have begun to multiply probabilities to analyze such situations.

Materials
- Student notebooks

continued on next page

Summarize
continued

• *What is the free-throw average for a player whose expected value is exactly 1?*

From the graph in Question C, it is approximately 62%. However, the change is not linear. Connect the points with a curved line.

ACE Assignment Guide for Problem 3.2

Differentiated Instruction
Solutions for All Learners

Core 4

Other *Applications* 5–7; *Connections* 16–19; *Extensions* 23–26, 28; unassigned choices from previous problems

Adapted For suggestions about adapting ACE exercises, see the CMP *Special Needs Handbook*.

Connecting to Prior Units Exercise 16: *Comparing and Scaling*; Exercises 18–19: *Accentuate the Negative*

Answers to Problem 3.2

A. 1. 40 times, 0 points

2. 24 times, 24 points

3. 36 times, 72 points

4. 96 points

5. 0.96 points per trip

B. 1.–2. The completed table is shown below. (Figure 1)

3. Possible patterns: As the player's average increases by 20%, the probability of getting 0 points decreases by 20%. As the averages increases, the average points per trip increases.

C. 1.

Points Expected in a One-and-One Situation

2. The average points per trip increases as the player's average increases.

3. His average is probably a little more than 60%.

4. A player with a 70% average has an expected value of 1.2 points per trip. Possible area model:

Figure 1   **Points Expected in 100 One-and-One Situations**

Player's Free-Throw Percentage	Points			Expected Value, or Average
	0 points	1 point	2 points	
20%	80%	16%	4%	0.24 points/trip
40%	60%	24%	16%	0.56 points/trip
60%	40%	24%	36%	0.96 points/trip
80%	20%	16%	64%	1.44 points/trip

Choosing Pay Plans

Mathematical Goals

- Practice determining the expected value in a probability situation

- Use probability to make decisions

This problem offers students four different situations to find expected value. The general setting is that two students cut lawns in the summer. Several of their customers offer different pay plans in place of their standard charge of $20 per lawn. They need to decide if these plans are greater than, equal to, or less than $20 per lawn. That is, they have to find the expected value for each situation.

Launch 3.3

Describe the situation to the students. You may want to ask if they have summer jobs and what they charge.

You may want to do Question A as a whole class. Then let the students explore the remaining three situations.

The situation in Question D is quite new to the students, since they are choosing twice from the same bag, *without replacement*. That is, what gets chosen the first time stays out of the bag so the probabilities for the second choice depend on what was chosen first. In this case, the bag contains 1 twenty-dollar bill and 3 one-dollar bills. You might want to demonstrate this situation to make sure the students understand the outcomes. While the only possible totals are $21 and $2, there are several ways to get each of these outcomes.

Let the students work in pairs.

Explore 3.3

Students could put their work on a large sheet of paper that shows their strategies.

Summarize 3.3

Call on different students to present their answers and their work. Have the rest of the class validate their reasoning. One good analysis is making a list.

Outcome	Probability	Payoff
HHH		
HHT	$\frac{1}{2}$	$25
HTH		
THH		
TTH		
THT	$\frac{1}{2}$	$15
HTT		
TTT		

Expected value is $\frac{1}{2}(25) + \frac{1}{2}(15) = \$20$.

Expected value is an important concept. It may be a bit challenging but students generally enjoy analyzing situations like those posed in this problem.

Check for Understanding

Ask students to describe another pay plan that can be analyzed by the class. Suggest that some students design a pay plan whose expected value is exactly $5. You could also have students work on ACE Exercise 8. For an extra challenge, have students alter each pay plan in that ACE exercise and in this problem to be better than the conventional alternative.

Choosing Pay Plans

Mathematical Goals

- Practice determining the expected value in a probability situation
- Use probability to make decisions

Launch

Describe the situation to the students. You may want to ask if they have summer jobs and what they charge.

The situation in Question D is quite new to the students, since they are choosing twice from the same bag, *without replacement*. That is, what gets chosen the first time stays out of the bag so the probabilities for the second choice depend on what was chosen first.

Let the students work in pairs.

Explore

Students could put their work on a large sheet of paper that shows their strategies.

Materials
- Large sheets of paper (optional)
- Markers (optional)

Summarize

Call on different students to present their answers and their work. Have the rest of the class validate their reasoning. One good analysis is making a list.

Materials
- Student notebooks

Outcome	Probability	Payoff	Expected Value
HHH			
HHT			
HTH	$\frac{1}{2}$	$25	
THH			
TTH			$\frac{1}{2} \times 25 + \frac{1}{2} \times 15 = \frac{1}{2}(40) = \$20$
THT			
HTT	$\frac{1}{2}$	$15	
TTT			

Check for Understanding

Ask students to describe another pay plan that can be analyzed by the class.

Core 8

Other *Connections* 9, 20–22; *Extensions* 27; unassigned choices from previous exercises

Adapted For suggestions about adapting ACE exercises, see the CMP *Special Needs Handbook*.

Answers to Problem 3.3

	G	R	B
R	RG	RR	RB
G	GG	GR	GB
B	BG	BR	BB
Y	YG	YR	YB

A. P(red and blue) $= \frac{2}{12}$;

P(neither red nor blue) $= \frac{10}{12}$;

$(2 \times \$24) + (10 \times \$10) = \$148$ and
$\$148 \div 12 \approx \$12.33$. REJECT because it is less than $20.

B. Because the expected amount of money would be $(\frac{1}{2} \times \$25) + (\frac{1}{2} \times \$18)$ and this is $21.50, ACCEPT because it comes out to be more than $20.

C. P(product is 24) $= \frac{2}{36}$; P(product not 24) $= \frac{34}{36}$; $(2 \times \$40) + (34 \times \$10) = \$420$; and $\$420 \div 36 \approx \$11.67$. REJECT because it is less than $20.

D. There are two different payments: $21 and $2. Consider the area model below, where the shaded regions represent a $21 payment.

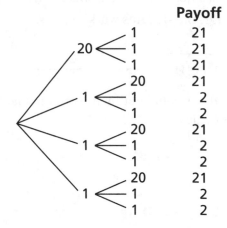

Another analysis:

$P(\$21) = \frac{6}{12}$; $P(\$2) = \frac{6}{12}$;

$(6 \times \$21) + (6 \times \$2) = \$138$; and
$\$138 \div 12 = \$11.50$. REJECT because it is less than $20.

E. P(two or more heads) $= \frac{4}{8}$;

P(less than 2 heads) $= \frac{4}{8}$;

$(4 \times \$25) + (4 \times \$15) = \$160$; and
$\$160 \div 8 = \$20$. ACCEPT or REJECT because this is what they thought customers should pay. The partners should expect that this plan will be the same as their original plan in the long run. In the short run, they could come out either ahead or behind.

The student edition pages for this investigation begin on the next page.

Notes _____

_____

_____

_____

Expected Value

On April 14, 1993, during halftime of a basketball game between the Chicago Bulls and the Miami Heat, Don Calhoun won $1 million by making a basket from the free-throw line at the opposite end of the court. Don was chosen at random to attempt the basket as part of a promotional contest. A *Sports Illustrated* article explained:

> *The odds against one randomly chosen person given one shot from the opposite foul line and making it are considered astronomical. Scottie Pippen admitted that after practice one day he and Michael Jordan tried to hit the shot but couldn't.*
>
> (Source: Bessone, Lisa, "Sports People: Don Calhoun." *Sports Illustrated*, April 26, 1993, vol 48.)

Fortunately, not every basket is this difficult to make! In this Investigation, you will use a player's free-throw percent to figure out what is likely to happen in a given free-throw situation.

3.1 One-and-One Free-Throws

In the district finals, Nishi's basketball team is 1 point behind with 2 seconds left. Nishi has just been fouled, and she is in a one-and-one free-throw situation. This means that Nishi will try one free throw. If she makes it, she tries a second free throw. If she misses the first time, she does not get a second try. Nishi's free-throw average is 60%.

38 What Do You Expect?

Notes _____

_____

_____

_____

- What are the possible scores Nishi can make in a one-and-one free-throw situation?
- How can each score be made?
- How would you design an experiment to analyze this situation?

Problem 3.1 Simulating a Probability Situation

A. Is it most likely that Nishi will score 0 points, 1 point, or 2 points? Record what you think before you analyze the situation.

B. Use this spinner to simulate Nishi's one-and-one situation 20 times. Record the result of each trial.

C. Based on your results, what is the experimental probability that Nishi will score 0 points? That she will score 1 point? That she will score 2 points?

D. Make an area model for this situation using a 10 × 10 grid. What is the theoretical probability that Nishi will score 0 points? That she will score 1 point? That she will score 2 points? Compare the three theoretical probabilities with the three experimental probabilities.

E. Suppose Nishi's free-throw average is 70%. How does this affect the outcome? Explain.

F. How does the diagram in Question D help you predict how many times Nishi will score 2 points in 100 one-and-one situations? In 200 one-and-one situations?

ACE Homework starts on page 43.

Investigation 3 Expected Value **39**

Notes _____

_____

_____

_____

In Problem 3.1, you looked at the probabilities of different outcomes of Nishi's one-and-one free-throw situation. You might have been surprised about which outcome is most likely. In this Problem, you will look at the number of points Nishi can expect to make each time she is in a one-and-one free-throw situation.

Problem 3.2 Finding Expected Value

Suppose Nishi has a 60% free-throw percentage and is in a one-and-one free-throw situation 100 times during the season.

A. **1.** How many times can she expect to score 0 points? What is the total number of points for these situations?

   2. How many times can she expect to score 1 point? What is the total number of points for these situations?

   3. How many times can she expect to score 2 points? What is the total number of points for these situations?

   4. What total number of points do you expect Nishi to score in these 100 situations at the free-throw line?

   5. What would Nishi's average number of points (expected value) per situation be?

Notes _____

_____

_____

_____

B. 1. In a one-and-one situation, what score is most likely to happen for a player whose free-throw percentage is 20%? 40%? 60%? 80%?

2. Copy and complete the table at the right for the players in part (1) in 100 one-and-one situations. You will fill in the expected value column in part (3).

3. Calculate the average number of points for each situation. Record these values in the table in part (2). Describe any pattern you see.

Points Expected in 100 One-and-One Situations

Player's Free-Throw Percentage	Points			Expected Value, or Average
	0	1	2	
20%	■	■	■	■
40%	■	■	■	■
60%	■	■	■	■
80%	■	■	■	■

C. 1. Make a graph like the one started at the right for each of the players in your table. Use your graph to answer parts (2)–(4).

2. How does the average number of points compare for players with a 20% free-throw percentage, a 40% free-throw percentage, a 60% free-throw percentage, and an 80% free-throw percentage?

3. Nishi's dad noticed that he makes an average of about 1 point in one-and-one free-throw situations. What is his free-throw percentage?

4. Nishi's older sister has a 70% free-throw percentage. What is her average number of points in one-and-one situations? Check your answer by making an area model.

Points Expected in a One-and-One Situation

ACE Homework starts on page 43.

3.3 Choosing Pay Plans

The average number of points in the one-and-one situation is the **expected value** for this situation. Expected value is used in a variety of other situations such as determining life-insurance premiums and lottery prizes, and for predicting gains and losses in businesses. The following problem shows another situation in which expected value is useful.

Notes _____

_____

_____

_____

Problem 3.3 Comparing Expected Values

Julie and Brandon cut lawns for their neighbors to earn money to donate to a local charity. They thought that customers should pay $20. However, several customers offered a different pay plan and asked the students to choose. Julie and Brandon have to decide which of the pay plans would give them a fair deal over the long run.

In each case, calculate the expected value. Then, decide whether they should accept or reject the pay plan. Give reasons for your decision.

A. The customer spins each of these spinners once. If one spinner is red and the other is blue (the order makes no difference), Julie and Brandon get $24. Otherwise, they get $10.

 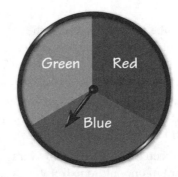

B. The customer rolls a pair of number cubes and adds the two numbers. If the sum is even, Julie and Brandon get $25. If it is odd, they get $18.

C. The customer rolls a pair of number cubes. If the product is 24, Julie and Brandon get $40. Otherwise, they get $10.

D. The customer places a twenty-dollar bill and three one-dollar bills in a bag. Julie and Brandon choose two bills. The money they choose is their payment.

E. The customer tosses three coins. If two or more land heads up, Julie and Brandon get $25. Otherwise, they get $15.

ACE Homework starts on page 43.

Notes _____

_____

_____

_____

Applications

In a one-and-one free-throw situation, is the player with each free-throw average most likely to score 0 points, 1 point, or 2 points? Make an area model to support each answer.

1. an 80% average

2. a 40% average

For Exercises 3–5, use the information in the table. It shows statistics for some of the players on a basketball team.

Free-Throw Statistics

Name	Free Throws Attempted	Free Throws Made
Gerrit	54	27
David	49	39
Ken	73	45
Alex	60	42

3. a. Which player has the best chance of making his next free throw? Explain your reasoning.

b. What is the free-throw probability for each player?

4. a. Alex has just been fouled and is in a one-and-one free-throw situation. What is the probability he will score 0 points? 1 point? 2 points?

b. Suppose Alex is in a one-and-one situation 100 times. How many times do you expect each of the outcomes in part (a) to occur?

c. What is the average number of points you expect Alex to make in a one-and-one situation?

d. Repeat part (a) using Gerrit.

5. a. In a different type of free-throw situation, a player gets a second attempt, even if the first free-throw is missed. Suppose Gerrit is in this two-attempt free-throw situation. What is the probability he will score 0 points? 1 point? 2 points?

b. Compare your answers to part (a) with Exercise 4(d). Explain why the answers are not exactly the same.

STUDENT PAGE

Notes _____

_____

_____

_____

6. Nishi, who has a 60% free-throw average, is in a two-attempt free-throw situation. Remember, this means that she will attempt the second free-throw no matter what happens on the first.

Homework
Help nline
PHSchool.com
For: Help with Exercise 6
Web Code: ane-7306

   a. Is Nishi most likely to score 0 points, 1 point, or 2 points? Explain.

   b. Nishi plans to keep track of her score on two-attempt free-throw situations. What average number of points can she expect to score in two-attempt situations?

7. Repeat Exercise 6 for the player with each free-throw average.

   a. a 50% average   **b.** an 80% average

8. In each of the following situations, the customer should pay $10 per week for newspapers. Drew, the paper carrier, has to decide which customer suggestions give him a fair deal over the long run. In each case, decide if Drew should accept or reject his customer's suggestion.

   a. The customer puts a ten-dollar bill and two one-dollar bills in a bag. Drew chooses two bills.

   b. Drew tosses three coins. If they are all heads or all tails, Drew gets $30. Otherwise, he gets $2.

   c. Drew rolls a pair of number cubes. If the sum is 7, Drew gets $50. Otherwise, he gets $2.

Notes _____

_____

_____

_____

Connections

A game show uses a large spinner with many sections. At least one section is labeled "bankrupt." If a player spins "bankrupt," he or she loses that turn and all his or her money. Carlota makes a version of the spinner at the right.

9. What is the probability that a player who spins the spinner one time will land on bankrupt?

10. What is the probability that a player who spins the spinner one time will get $500 or more?

11. Sam just spun the spinner and it landed on $350. What is the probability he will land on $350 on his next spin? Explain your reasoning.

Multiple Choice For Exercises 12–14, choose the answer that is the correct percent of the given number.

12. 30% of 90

    A. 60   **B.** 27   **C.** 30   **D.** 3

13. 25% of 80

    F. 20   **G.** 3.2   **H.** 0.3175   **J.** 200

14. 45% of 180

    A. 2.5   **B.** 40   **C.** 81   **D.** 4

Go Online
PHSchool.com
For: Multiple-Choice Skills Practice
Web Code: ana-7254

15. Wanda, the Channel 1 weather person, said there was a 30% chance of rain on Saturday and a 30% chance of rain on Sunday. It rained both days, and Wanda's station manager is wondering if she should fire Wanda.

    a. Suppose Wanda's calculations were correct and there was a 30% chance of rain each day. What was the probability that there would be rain on both days?

    b. Do you think Wanda should be fired? Why or why not?

    c. Wanda is working on her predictions for the next few days. She calculates that there is a 20% chance of rain on Monday and a 20% chance of rain on Tuesday. If she is correct, what is the probability that it will rain on at least one of these days?

16. A lake has 10,000 fish. When a fisherman scoops up his net, he catches 500 fish. Suppose 150 of the 500 fish in his net are salmon. How many salmon do you predict are in the lake?

Investigation 3 Expected Value   **45**

Notes _____

_____

_____

_____

17. a. Copy the table below. Use your answers from Problem 3.2, Question C to fill in your table.

Probability of One Basket	20%	40%	60%	80%	100%
Average Points per One-and-One Attempt	0.24	▪	0.96	▪	▪

b. Is the average for 80% twice that of 40%?

c. Use this table or your graph from Problem 3.2, Question C. Is the average for 100% twice the average of 50%?

d. A player with a 20% free-throw average makes 0.24 points, on average, in a one-and-one situation. Copy and complete this table. How are the relationships in this table different from the table in part (a)?

Number of One-and-One Situations by a Player With a 20% Average	1	10	20	100
Average Points Made	0.24	▪	▪	▪

For Exercises 18 and 19, spin each spinner once. Use the spinners below.

18. Suppose you add the results.

a. What is the probability of getting a positive number?

b. What is the average value?

19. Suppose you multiply the results.

a. What is the probability of getting a positive number?

b. What is the average value?

20. Fred and Joseph are experimenting with a new game. The probability Fred wins a round of this game is $\frac{1}{3}$ and the probability Joseph wins a round is $\frac{2}{3}$. They decide that to make the game fair, Fred scores 3 points when he wins a round, and Joseph scores 2 points when he wins a round.

a. They play 12 rounds of the game. How many points can Fred expect to win? How many points can Joseph expect to win?

46 What Do You Expect?

b. How many points per round can each player expect to win? That is, what is the expected value for each player?

c. Is this a game in which Fred and Joseph have an equally-likely chance of making a winning total? Why or why not?

21. Ms. Rodriguez brought her dog to the vet for a distemper test. The test is correct 80% of the time. This means that 20% of the time the test of a dog with distemper indicates no distemper. The vet decides to test the dog twice.

a. If the dog has distemper, what is the probability that both tests will indicate no distemper? (It may help to make an area model of this situation.)

b. If the dog has distemper, what is the probability that at least one of the tests will indicate distemper?

22. A computer places a dot at random on a dartboard that is divided into four regions, A, B, C, and D. The dot has the same probability of being in region B, region C, or region D. The probability that the dot will be in region A is 40%.

a. What is the probability that the dot will *not* be in region A?

b. Make a square dartboard that meets the given conditions.

c. Make a circular dartboard that meets the given conditions.

Extensions

For Exercises 23 and 24, use the data about the basketball team from Exercises 3–5.

23. What is the probability that Alex will make all of his next three free throws? Explain your reasoning.

24. David is in a one-and-one free-throw situation. What is the probability that he will make both free-throws?

25. Emilio increases his free-throw average to 50%. His coach makes a deal with him. At tomorrow's practice, Emilio can attempt either to make three free throws in a row or to make at least four out of five free throws. If he is successful, he will start every game for the rest of the season. Which option should he choose? Explain.

Notes
_____
_____
_____
_____

26. a. Curt has made 60% of his free throws during recent practice sessions. The coach says that if Curt makes three free throws in a row, he can start Saturday's game. What is the probability that Curt will start Saturday's game?

b. Curt has a difficult time making three free throws in a row. The coach tells him to instead try making three out of four free throws. What is the probability that Curt will make at least three out of four free throws?

27. Natalie designs a carnival spinner game with 38 congruent sectors; 18 orange, 18 blue, and 2 white. A player pays $1 to play. The player picks either orange or blue. If the spinner stops on the chosen color, the player wins $2. If the spinner lands on any other color, the player does not get any money.

a. What is the probability that a player will lose on one spin of the wheel?

b. If a player plays the game many times, what is the average amount of money the player can expect to win or lose per spin of the wheel?

28. When a player is fouled while attempting a three-point basket, three free throws are awarded. Luis has an 80% free-throw average. He draws the diagrams below to analyze the probability of getting 1, 2, or 3 baskets.

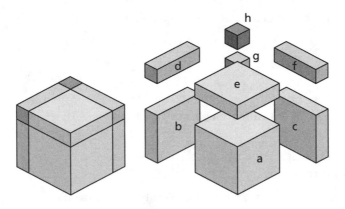

a. Which parts of the lettered diagram represent Luis making all three baskets? Exactly two baskets? Exactly one basket? Missing all three baskets?

b. What is the probability of Luis getting 1 point in a three free-throw situation? 2 points? 3 points? No points?

Notes _____

_____

_____

_____

Mathematical Reflections 3

In this investigation, you learned how to find the average outcome for events, such as a basketball player attempting free throws in a one-and-one situation. The following questions will help you summarize what you have learned.

Think about your answers to these questions. Discuss your ideas with other students and your teacher. Then write a summary of your findings in your notebook.

1. Expected value is sometimes called the long-term average. Explain why this makes sense.

2. Describe how you would calculate the expected value for a probability situation.

3. Explain how expected value can be useful.

Notes _____

_____

_____

_____

Investigation 3

ACE Assignment Choices

Problem 3.1
Core 1–3, 15
Other *Connections* 10–14

Problem 3.2
Core 4
Other *Applications* 5–7; *Connections* 16–19; *Extensions* 23–26, 28; unassigned choices from previous problems

Problem 3.3
Core 8
Other *Connections* 9, 20–22; *Extensions* 27; unassigned choices from previous exercises

Adapted For suggestions about adapting Exercise 3 and other ACE exercises, see the CMP *Special Needs Handbook*
Connecting to Prior Units 12–15: *Bits and Pieces III*; 16: *Comparing and Scaling*; 18–19: *Accentuate the Negative*

Applications

1. This player is most likely to score 2 points.

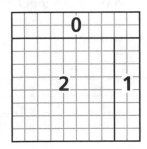

2. This player is most likely to score 0 points.

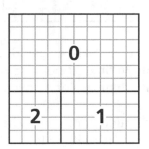

3. a. David has the best chance of making his next free throw, as his percent of baskets made is the highest.

b. Gerrit 50%, David 79.6%, Ken 61.6%, Alex 70%

4. a. $P(0 \text{ points}) = 30\%$; $P(1 \text{ point}) = 21\%$; $P(2 \text{ points}) = 49\%$

b. 0 points: 30 times; 1 point: 21 times; and 2 points: 49 times.

c. The average number of points he could expect per trip is $119 \div 100 = 1.19$.

d. Students may want to use 10 by 10 grids.
$P(0 \text{ points}) = 50\%$
$P(1 \text{ point}) = 25\%$
$P(2 \text{ points}) = 25\%$

5. a. Students may want to use a tree diagram.
$P(0 \text{ points}) = 25\%$; $P(1 \text{ point}) = 50\%$; $P(2 \text{ points}) = 25\%$

b. The probabilities for making both free throws in the two situations are equal. Gerrit can score 1 point by either making the first free throw and missing the second, or missing the first free throw and making the second. The fact that he automatically gets a second free throw increases his probability of getting 1 point and reduces his probability of getting 0 points.

6. a. Nishi is most likely to score 1 point.

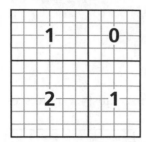

b. In 100 attempts, Nishi could expect to score 2 points 36 times, 1 point 48 times, and 0 points 16 times, for an overall total of 36(2) + 48(1) + 16(0) = 120 points. The average number of points she could expect per trip is thus 120 ÷ 100 = 1.2.

7. a. A player with a 50% free-throw average would be most likely to score 1 point.

b. A player with an 80% free-throw average would be most likely to get 2 points, getting 1.6 points per situation.

8. a. $P(\$11) = \frac{4}{6}$ or $\frac{2}{3}$; $P(\$2) = \frac{2}{6}$ or $\frac{1}{3}$. Make sure students realize that the two one-dollar bills must be treated as two separate bills, so that there are 6 total outcomes. The expected value per week is (2 × $11) + (1 × $2) = $24 total for 3 weeks. 24 ÷ 3 gives $8 per week. Drew should REJECT this proposal.

b. $P(\text{all same}) = \frac{2}{8}$ or $\frac{1}{4}$; $P(\text{not all the same}) = \frac{6}{8}$ or $\frac{3}{4}$. The expected value per week is (1 × $30) + (3 × $2) = $36 total for 4 weeks. 36 ÷ 4 gives $9 per week. Drew should REJECT this proposal.

c. $P(\text{sum of 7}) = \frac{6}{36}$ or $\frac{1}{6}$; $P(\text{sum is not 7}) = \frac{30}{36}$ or $\frac{5}{6}$. The expected value per week is (1 × $50) + (5 × $2) = $60 total. $60 per week for 6 weeks = $10.00 per week. Drew could ACCEPT or REJECT this proposal, as it will result in an average of $10 per week in the long run. In the short run, the results could be greater or less than $10 per week.

Connections

9. Each section is equally likely, so there is a 1 in 10, or 10%, chance of landing on bankrupt.

10. Three of the 10 sections have a value of $500 or more, so the probability of getting at least $500 on one spin is $\frac{3}{10}$, or 30%.

11. It is still 10%. Each player has a 10% chance of hitting $350 on each spin.

12. B   **13.** F   **14.** C

15. a. As shown in the area model below, the probability that it would rain on both days is 9%.

b. According to Wanda's predictions, there was a 9% chance that it would rain on both days. Thus, while it was unlikely that it would rain both days, it was not impossible. Wanda's knowledge should not be in question just because she didn't predict something that had only a 9% chance of happening.

c. As shown in the area model below, there is a 36% chance that it will rain on at least one of the two days.

16. 3,000 salmon, since $\frac{150}{500} = \frac{3,000}{10,000}$

17. a. (Figure 2)

b. No. The average for a player with an 80% average is more than twice that of a player with a 40% average.

c. Either from the table or the graph we can see that the average points for a player with a 50% average has to be between 0.56 and 0.96. This is not half the average points for a player with a 100% average.

d. This table shows that the rate stays the same, no matter how many free throws are taken. So if the player takes 50 free throws the average made will be half the average if the player takes 100 free throws.

Number of One-and-One Situations by a Player With a 20% Average	1	10	20	100
Average Points Made	0.24	2.4	4.8	24

18. a. $\frac{5}{9}$ **b.** 0

19. a. $\frac{5}{9}$ **b.** 0

20. a. If they play the game 12 times, Fred could expect to win $\frac{1}{3} \times 12 = 4$ times and Joseph $\frac{2}{3} \times 12 = 8$ times. Fred can expect to score $3 \times 4 = 12$ points, and Joseph can expect to score $2 \times 8 = 16$ points.

b. Fred can expect to score $12 \div 12 = 1$ point per game, and Joseph can expect to score $16 \div 12 \approx 1.33$ points per game.

c. This is not a fair game because Fred and Joseph do not have the same expected score per game.

21. a. As shown in the area model below, there is a 4% chance that both tests will say that the dog does not have distemper.

b. In the area model, 4 squares indicate two negative test results; the remaining 96 squares represent a positive test result. The probability that at least one test will indicate that the dog has distemper is 96%.

22. a. 60%

b. Possible answers (region A must occupy 40% and regions B, C, and D must each occupy 20%):

c. Possible answer:

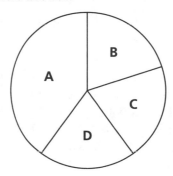

Figure 2

Probability of One Basket	20%	40%	60%	80%	100%
Average Points per One-and-One Attempt	0.24	0.56	0.96	1.44	2.0

Extensions

23. Approximately 34%; the probability that Alex will make one free throw is 70%, or $\frac{7}{10}$. Out of 100 sets of three free throws, he will make the first free throw about 70% of the time, or 70 times. Out of those 70 times, he will make the second free throw about 70% of the time, or $0.7 \times 70 = 49$ times. Out of those 49 times, he will make the third free throw about 70% of the time, or $0.7 \times 49 =$ about 34 times. Thus, the probability that he will make his next three free throws is about 34%.

24. Approximately 64%; David's free-throw average is 79.6%, or about 80%. Out of 100 attempts, David can expect to make 80 of his first free throws. Of his 80 second free throws, he can expect to make the second free throw 80% of the time, or about 64 times. This gives him about a 64% chance of making both free throws. (Note: Students might also multiply probabilities: $\frac{39}{49} \times \frac{39}{49} = \frac{1,521}{2,401} \approx 63.3\%$.)

25. He should choose the option that allows him to make 4 out of 5.

    The probability of Emilio getting 3 in a row is $\frac{1}{8}$. However, there are 32 equally likely outcomes for 5 free throws. Of these 32 outcomes, 6 are successful (hitting all five, missing the first free throw and hitting the rest, missing the second free throw and hitting the rest, etc.) Therefore, the probability that he will get 4 out of 5 is $\frac{6}{32} > \frac{1}{8}$.

26. **a.** The probability that Curt will make three free throws in a row is $0.6 \times 0.6 \times 0.6 = 0.216$, or 21.6%.

    b. Approximately 48%; there are four ways Curt could make three free throws and miss one. The probability that Curt will miss any one free throw is 40% or 0.4, so the probability that he will miss any one specific free throw and make the other three is $0.4 \times 0.6 \times 0.6 \times 0.6 = 0.0864$, or 8.64%. For all four ways he could miss one free throw. This is a combined probability of $4 \times 8.64\% = 34.56\%$. Curt could also make all four free throws, with a probability of $0.6 \times 0.6 \times 0.6 \times 0.6 = 0.1296$, or 12.96%.

The probability, then, that he will make at least three out of four free throws is $34.56\% + 12.96\% = 47.52\%$.

27. **a.** A player can pick either blue or orange. In either case, there are 18 ways to win and 20 ways to lose, so the probability of winning on one spin is $\frac{18}{38}$, or about 0.47, and the probability of losing is about 0.53.

    b. A player can expect to win $2 on 18 out of 38 spins, a total of $36. This is an expected value of $36 ÷ 38 spins = about $0.95 per spin, so the player can expect to lose about $0.05 per spin.

28. **a.** 3 free throws: a
    2 free throws: b, c, and e
    1 free throw: d, f, and g
    0 free throws: h

    b. $P(1 \text{ point}) = 0.096$ $P(2 \text{ points}) = 0.384$
    $P(3 \text{ points}) = 0.512$ $P(0 \text{ points}) = 0.008$

Possible Answers to Mathematical Reflections

1. The *expected value* is what you *could expect* to happen in the *long run*. That is, it is the average taken over a large number of attempts.

2. To find expected value, you need to know the number of times something can be expected to happen out of 100 (or the percent) and the points awarded when it happens. To find the number of times an outcome will occur, you multiply the probability of the outcome times the number of times the situation might occur.

   For example, in 100 trips, shooting the one-and-one, the 70% shooter could expect to score 0 points 30 times, 1 point 21 times, and 2 points 49 times, for a total of $21 + 2(49) = 119$ points. This would give him a long-term average or expected value of $119 ÷ 100 = 1.19$ points per trip. His expected value is 1.19, since this is the number of points he could expect to earn on average per trip to the line over the long run.

3. Expected value helps you predict what is most likely to happen over the long run; it is a good estimate for probability situations that have a payoff. It helps you make decisions during games of chance, in sports by determining who is the best person to attempt a technical foul, and in predicting the weather, which is based on the average outcomes of certain conditions.

Businesses could use it to predict profits or losses. Businesses that manufacture products use expected value in quality control. A business might decide how many defective products they can tolerate in a large sample and then calculate the expected value (cost to the company) to replace the defective products.

Mathematical and Problem-Solving Goals

- Analyze a binomial situation

- Practice finding expected value in a multiple-stage probability situation

- Analyze a binomial situation with multiple-stage outcomes

In this investigation, students analyze binomial situations that are essentially the same such as tossing a coin, a child being born (boy or girl), or guessing on a true/false test. The probabilities of the outcomes in each of these situations are equally likely.

Summary of Problems

Problem 4.1 Guessing Answers

Students are introduced to binomial outcomes by taking a four-item true/false quiz on which they must generate their answers at random.

Problem 4.2 Ortonville

Students analyze all the combinations of boys and girls in families in the fictitious town of Ortonville. Each family has exactly five children.

Problem 4.3 A Baseball Series

Students analyze the last five games in a baseball series where each team has a 50% chance of winning for each game and consider the probabilities of the series ending in various numbers of games.

	Suggested Pacing	Materials for Students	Materials for Teachers	ACE Assignments
All	4 days	Student notebooks	Transparency markers	
4.1	1 day	Pennies (1 per student)		1, 2, 11
4.2	$1\frac{1}{2}$ days		Transparency 4.2 (optional)	3–8, 9, 12–13, 18–22
4.3	1 day			10, 14–17
MR	$\frac{1}{2}$ day			

4.1 Guessing Answers

Goals

- Analyze a binomial situation
- Practice finding expected value in a multiple-stage probability situation

In this problem students take a four-item true/false quiz. They toss a coin to determine an answer of true or false. If the penny turns up heads, the students write "True." If the penny turns up tails, the students write "False." The teacher then gives the students the "correct" answers. Students score their papers and then calculate the expected value (or the average score) for guessing at random in a four-item true/false quiz.

Launch 4.1

A fun way to launch this problem is by announcing to the class that they are going to take a short quiz that contains four true/false questions. Ask the students to put their names on a piece of paper and list the numbers 1 to 4 so that they can record their answers to the quiz. Now pretend to look for the quiz and after a bit of shuffling papers around on your desk, tell the class that you must have left the quiz at home. The class will probably be relieved. But then tell the class that they can take the quiz anyway. Now, they will be puzzled.

To do this, tell them they will toss a penny. If the penny turns up heads, the student writes "True." If the penny turns up tails, the student writes "False." Give the class a bit of time to determine their answers. Once this is done, give the class the correct answers, which you should generate at random either ahead of time or in front of the class.

Tell them to mark each question with correct or incorrect. The language is a bit tricky. Students first record their answers either true or false. Next they use the teacher's key to mark each of their answers as correct (C) or incorrect (X). It is helpful to discuss answers as correct and incorrect rather than true and false.

Collect all the scores on the board. Ask that each student make a record.

Tell the class that each item counts for 25 points. A perfect paper (all correct) is 100 points, or 100%.

You can now analyze the experimental probability of getting a score of

- 100% (all correct)
- 75% (exactly three correct)
- 50% (exactly two correct)
- 25% (exactly one correct)
- 0% (all incorrect)

If you prefer, you can just pose the question of what score the class would expect to get on a true/false item quiz if they guessed at random at all of the answers. Collect some responses. Then have students generate their random answers, give the correct answers, and help the class to interpret the examples.

The students can now work in pairs to find the outcomes and the theoretical probabilities.

Explore 4.1

Students may need help analyzing theoretical outcomes. They can use tree diagrams or tables which are easier to interpret. Students may also need help in interpreting results. Help them to label each outcome as 4 correct, 3 correct, 2 correct, 1 correct, and 0 correct. See the summary for more comments on how to organize and interpret a table.

Summarize 4.1

Ask groups to explain how they analyzed their list of combinations of right and wrong answers for a four-question true/false quiz.

If this was not done in the launch, collect the data from the class about their answers. Record the number of students who got 4 correct, 3 correct, 2 correct, 1 correct, and 0 correct.

Suggested Question Ask the class how they could find the theoretical probabilities. Collect a few suggestions.

- *How many ways can you get exactly three correct?* (CCCX, CCXC, CXCC, or XCCC.)

For this situation, making a list or a tree diagram of all the possibilities will work. In any case, you will need to help the students make sense of the 16 possibilities (Figure 1).

You may need to help the class compute the expected value (average score) in Question C part (2).

Suggested Question Ask:

- *What does expected value mean in this situation?* (If you always guess the answers on a four-item true/false quiz, the expected value is the average score you would expect to receive.)

Have the class discuss what might happen on a 5-item (or 2- or 3-item) true/false quiz. You could also discuss a 1-item, 2-item, and 3-item true/false quiz. Ask groups to explain how they analyzed their list of combinations of right and wrong answers for a four-question true/false quiz. If you do this, organize the data in some way so students begin to see binomial patterns. (See Pascal's Triangle in Extension Exercises 18–22.)

Figure 1

4 correct	3 correct	2 correct	1 correct	0 correct
CCCC	CCCX	CCXX	CXXX	XXXX
	CCXC	CXCX	XCXX	
	CXCC	CXXC	XXCX	
	XCCC	XCXC	XXXC	
		XCCX		
		XXCC		

Mathematical Goals

- Analyze a binomial situation
- Practice finding expected value in a multiple-stage probability situation

Launch

Ask the students to put their names on a piece of paper and list the numbers 1 to 4 so that they can record their answers to the quiz. Tell them they will toss a penny. If the penny turns up heads, the student writes "True." If the penny turns up tails, the student writes "False." Give the class a bit of time to determine their answers. Once this is done, give the class the correct answers, which you should generate at random either ahead of time or in front of the class.

Tell them to mark each question with correct or incorrect.

Collect all the scores on the board. Ask that each student make a record. Tell the class that each item counts for 25 points. A perfect paper (all correct) is 100 points or 100%.

Analyze the experimental probability of getting each possible score.

If you prefer, you can just pose the question of what score the class would expect to get on a true/false item quiz if they guessed at random at all of the answers. Collect some responses. Then have students generate their random answers, give the correct answers, and help the class to interpret the examples. The students can now work in pairs to find the outcomes and the theoretical probabilities.

Materials
- Pennies

Explore

Students may need help analyzing theoretical outcomes. They can use tree diagrams or tables which are easier to interpret. Students may also need help in interpreting each result. Help them to label each outcome as 4 correct, 3 correct, 2 correct, 1 correct, and 0 correct. See the summary for more comments on how to organize and interpret a table.

Materials

Summarize

Ask the class how to find the theoretical probabilities. Collect a few suggestions.

- *How many ways can you get exactly three correct?*

For this situation, making a list or a tree diagram of all of the possibilities will work. In any case, you will need to help the students make sense of the 16 possibilities.

You may need to help the class compute the expected value (average score) in Question C part (2). Ask:

- *What does expected value mean in this situation?*

Materials
- Student notebooks

continued on next page

Discuss what might happen on a 5-item (or 2- or 3-item) true/false quiz. You could also discuss a 1-item, 2-item, and 3-item true/false quiz. Ask groups to explain how they analyzed their list of combinations of right and wrong answers for a four-question true/false quiz

ACE Assignment Guide for Problem 4.1

Core 11
Other *Applications* 1, 2

Adapted For suggestions about adapting ACE exercises, see the CMP *Special Needs Handbook*.
Connecting to Prior Units 11: *How Likely Is It?*

Answers to Problem 4.1

A. Answers will vary. *Exactly 2 correct* is the most likely outcome and, in a large number of experiments, should represent between a third and a half of all papers.

B. **1.** 1 incorrect answer: 4
    2 incorrect answers: 6
    3 incorrect answers: 4
    4 incorrect answers: 1
    4 correct answers: 1

2. a. $P(\text{score of } 100) = \frac{1}{16}$

b. $P(\text{score of } 75) = \frac{4}{16}$ or $\frac{1}{4}$

c. $P(\text{score of } 50) = \frac{6}{16}$

d. $P(\text{score of } 25) = \frac{4}{16}$ or $\frac{1}{4}$

e. $P(\text{score of } 0) = \frac{1}{16}$

C. 1–2. a. You would expect to get four correct
    $32 \times (\frac{1}{16}) = 2$ times, so you would get
    $2 \times 100 = 200$ points.

b. You would expect to get three correct
    $32 \times (\frac{1}{4}) = 8$ times and would get
    $75 \times 8 = 600$ points.

c. You would expect to get two correct
    $32 \times (\frac{6}{16}) = 12$ times, so you would get
    $12 \times 50 = 600$ points.

d. You would expect to get one correct
    $32 \times (\frac{1}{4}) = 8$ times, so you would get
    $25 \times 8 = 200$ points.

e. You would expect to get zero correct
    $32 \times (\frac{1}{16}) = 2$ times, so you would get
    0 points.

3. One possible answer:

For taking the quiz 32 times:
$(\frac{1}{16} \times 32)(100) + (\frac{4}{16} \times 32)(75) +$

$(\frac{6}{16} \times 32)(50) + (\frac{4}{16} \times 32)(25) +$

$(\frac{1}{16} \times 32)(0) = 200 + 600 + 600 +$

$200 + 0 = 1,600$
$\frac{1,600}{32} = 50$ points per quiz.

For taking the quiz 100 times, the expected value will not change:
$(\frac{1}{16} \times 100)(100) + (\frac{4}{16} \times 100)(75) +$

$(\frac{6}{16} \times 100)(50) + (\frac{4}{16} \times 100)(25) +$

$(\frac{1}{16} \times 100)(0) = 5,000$
$\frac{5,000}{100} = 50$ points per quiz.

The averages were the same because the probabilities and payoffs did not change. Also, the number of times the quiz was taken increased in proportion to the total number of points in each situation: $\frac{1,000}{20} = \frac{5,000}{100}$, this keeps the average points the same.

D. $P(\text{all five questions correct}) = \frac{1}{32}$

4.2 Ortonville

Mathematical Goal

- Analyze a binomial situation

In this problem, students analyze all of the combinations of boys and girls in families in Ortonville that all have exactly five children.

Launch 4.2

Define binomial probabilities. Tell the class about the special features of Ortonville. Each family is named Orton and has exactly five children. Each family also agrees to name their children in a special order.

Suggested Questions Ask the class the following questions:

- *Do any of you come from a family of five children?*

- *What is the order of boys and girls?*

- *What are their names?*

Show the list of names for Ortonville.

Ask for a combination of boys and girls for a family of five. Show how the names are assigned. For example, if the family is BBGGB, then the names are Benson, Berndt, Gail, Gerry, and Brett.

Challenge the class to find all the combinations for five children. Have students work on listing all the possible combinations in pairs. They can work on the questions in groups of two or three.

Explore 4.2

Remind groups to give reasons to support their answers.

Many students will be able to find all the possibilities by using a systematic listing strategy. However, using tree diagrams for simple situations can help students to understand how to make a complete list without making a tree diagram. If some students are having difficulty listing the possibilities, help them to get started making a tree diagram for a smaller family of three or four.

Students may have found the systematic listing done for Problem 4.1 helpful in finding all the combinations for the families.

Help students label their information, such as 5 girls–0 boys, 4 girls–1 boy, 3 girls–2 boys, 2 girls–3 boys, 1 girl–4 boys, 0 girls–5 boys. Some students may notice that they need not write both the number of boys and of girls; saying "4 girls" is the same as saying "4 girls–1 boy."

Some students may struggle with the *or* condition in Question C. Keep an eye out for students who misinterpret *or* to exclude combinations like BGGGB. in part (3). The mathematical "or" is an and/or.

Summarize 4.2

Ask the class to share their strategies for finding all 32 combinations.

Suggested Questions

- *Why are there 32 outcomes?*

Call on different students to provide answers to the questions.

- *How is this situation similar to taking a true/false test? To tossing a coin?*

Tell the class that these are all binomial situations. There are two outcomes at each stage. In this case, each outcome is equally likely, but this is not always the case in a binomial situation.

- *Are there other examples of binomial situations?* (The spinner games Match/No-Match and Making Purple are examples. Lights on and off is another.)

- *Why is this a good name for these situations? Why binomial?*

Save the table of the 32 possibilities for the next problem and for Extension Exercise 20.

Going Further

This would be a good time to develop Pascal's Triangle. See ACE Exercises 18–22.

4.2 Ortonville

Mathematical Goal

- Analyze a binomial situation

Launch

Tell the class about the special features of Ortonville. Each family is named Orton and has exactly five children. Each family also agrees to name their children in a special order. Ask the class,

- *Do any of you come from a family of five children?*
- *What is the order of boys and girls?*
- *What are their names?*

Show the list of names for Ortonville.

Ask for a combination of boys and girls for a family of five. Show how the names are assigned.

Challenge the class to find all of the combinations for five children. Have students work on listing all the possible combinations in pairs. They can work on the questions in groups of two or three.

Materials

- Transparency 4.2

Vocabulary

- binomial situation

Explore

Remind groups to give reasons to support their answers.

Many students will be able to find all the possibilities by using a systematic listing strategy. However, using tree diagrams for simple situations can help students to understand how to make a complete list without making a tree diagram. If some students are having difficulty listing the possibilities, help them to get started making a tree diagram for a smaller family of three or four.

Help students label their information such as 5 girls–0 boys, 4 girls–1 boy, 3 girls–2 boys, 2 girls–3 boys, 1 girl–4 boys, 0 girls–5 boys.

Summarize

Ask the class to share their strategies for finding all 32 combinations. Call on different students to provide answers to the questions. Ask

- *How is this situation similar to taking a true/false test? To tossing a coin?*

Tell the class that these are all binomial situations. There are two outcomes at each stage. In this case, each outcome is equally likely, but this is not always the case in a binomial situation.

- *Are there other examples of binomial situations?*
- *Why is this a good name for these situations? Why binomial?*

Going Further

This would be a good time to develop Pascal's Triangle. See ACE Exercises 18–22.

Materials

- Student notebooks

Core 3–8

Other *Applications* 9, *Connections* 12–13;
Extensions 18–22; unassigned choices from
previous problems

Adapted For suggestions about adapting ACE
exercises, see the CMP *Special Needs Handbook*.

Answers to Problem 4.2

A. There are $2 \times 2 \times 2 \times 2 \times 2 = 2^5 = 32$
possible combinations.

5 girls, 0 boys:

Gloria, Gilda, Gail, Gerry, Gina

4 girls, 1 boy:

Gloria, Gilda, Gail, Gerry, Brett
Gloria, Gilda, Gail, Blake, Gina
Gloria, Gilda, Blair, Gerry, Gina
Gloria, Berndt, Gail, Gerry, Gina
Benson, Gilda, Gail, Gerry, Gina

3 girls, 2 boys:

Gloria, Gilda, Gail, Blake, Brett
Gloria, Gilda, Blair, Gerry, Brett
Gloria, Berndt, Gail, Gerry, Brett
Benson, Gilda, Gail, Gerry, Brett
Gloria, Gilda, Blair, Blake, Gina
Gloria, Berndt, Gail, Blake, Gina
Benson, Gilda, Gail, Blake, Gina
Gloria, Berndt, Blair, Gerry, Gina
Benson, Gilda, Blair, Gerry, Gina
Benson, Berndt, Gail, Gerry, Gina

2 girls, 3 boys:

Gloria, Gilda, Blair, Blake, Brett
Gloria, Berndt, Gail, Blake, Brett
Gloria, Berndt, Blair, Gerry, Brett
Gloria, Berndt, Blair, Blake, Gina
Benson, Gilda, Gail, Blake, Brett
Benson, Gilda, Blair, Gerry, Brett
Benson, Gilda, Blair, Blake, Gina
Benson, Berndt, Gail, Gerry, Brett
Benson, Berndt, Gail, Blake, Gina
Benson, Berndt, Blair, Gerry, Gina

1 girl, 4 boys:

Gloria, Berndt, Blair, Blake, Brett
Benson, Gilda, Blair, Blake, Brett
Benson, Berndt, Gail, Blake, Brett
Benson, Berndt, Blair, Gerry, Brett
Benson, Berndt, Blair, Blake, Gina

0 girls, 5 boys:

Benson, Berndt, Blair, Blake, Brett

B. $P(\text{Gloria, Gilda, Blair, Blake, Gina}) = \frac{1}{32}$

C. 1. $P(\text{exactly 5 girls}) = \frac{1}{32}$;

$P(\text{exactly five boys}) = \frac{1}{32}$

2. $P(\text{two girls and three boys}) = \frac{10}{32}$

3. $P(\text{first or last child a boy}) = \frac{24}{32}$

4. $P(\text{at least one boy}) = \frac{31}{32}$

5. $P(\text{at most one boy}) = \frac{6}{32}$

A Baseball Series

Mathematical Goal

• Analyze a binomial situation with multiple-stage outcomes

In this problem students analyze the last five games in a baseball series where each team has a 50% chance of winning for each game. One team has won the first two games. Students use lists or tree diagrams to determine the outcomes.

Launch 4.3

Tell the class about the baseball series between the Bobcats and the Gazelles.

Suggested Questions

• *What is the probability of the series ending in 4 games? 5 games? 6 games? 7 games?*

Have students make their predictions.

• *Who has the greater chance of winning—the Bobcats or the Gazelles?*

• *How is this similar to, and different from, Problem 4.2?*

One way to show what has happened is to write GG_ _ _ _ _.

• *There are five games left. How can we predict what will happen in the third game? Fourth game? Etc.?*

Some students may suggest tossing a coin since it represents a 50% chance of heads or tails. Toss a coin five times to get an example of what could happen.
For example, GG <u>GBBBG</u>. Ask them:

• *Who wins the series?* (Gazelles)

• *How long is the series?* (seven games)

Suggested Questions Ask:

• *How many different ways could the remaining five games play out?* (You could generate a few more examples by continuing to toss the coin.)

• *How might the data from the last problem be helpful for this situation?* [All the B/G (Boy/Girl) combinations are just like the B/G (Bobcats/Gazelles) in this problem.]

Students may begin to see that this is just like the last problem. Finding all the combinations of boy and girl in a family with five children is just like finding all of the ways the remaining five games of the baseball series plays out between the Bobcats and Gazelles. These are both binomial situations.

Pick a few of the B/G combinations and help the class interpret them in terms of a baseball series. They need to know how long the series went and which team has the greater probability of winning.

For example, a helpful recording scheme might be: GGBBB 4–G (ends in four games and the Gazelles win)

BBGBB 7–B (ends in seven games and the Bobcats win)

Let the class work in pairs.

Explore 4.3

Make sure everyone is analyzing the data correctly and has a valid recording scheme.

Summarize 4.3

Students will be surprised that the probability of the series ending in four, five, six, or seven games is the same, $\frac{1}{4}$ or $\frac{8}{32}$. But the Gazelles have a greater chance of winning the series.

If the Gazelles win games 3 and 4, some students may wonder why you have to count all of the following possibilities for the remaining five games:

GGGGG	GGGGB
GGBGG	GGBGB
GGBBG	GGGBB
GGBBB	GGGBG

The series clearly ends in four games and the Gazelles win. This is difficult to explain, but all eight possibilities need to be listed in order to properly weight the probabilities. The difficulty is that if we only list the games necessary to finish the series, we get 16 outcomes:

4 games	5 games	6 games	7 games
GG	GBG	GBBG	BBBGG
	BGG	BGBG	BBGBG
		BGBG	BGBBG
		BBGG	GBBBG
		BBBB	GBBBB
			BGBBB
			BBGBB
			BBBGB

However, these outcomes are not equally likely. For instance the Bobcats winning the next two games (BB) is just as likely as the Gazelles winning them (GG), but GG is counted in five different outcomes, while BB is counted only once. These five GG outcomes *together* must be as likely as the one BB outcome.

A different way to see what is going on is to make a weighted tree. If this question comes up and you have discussed weighted trees, then you can use this method to show all of the possibilities.

Consider the portion of a tree below. The GGGG branch of the tree starting on the left represents the Gazelles winning in four games. The next branch down, GGGBG, represents one way that the Gazelles could win in five games. These two branches are not equally likely. The GGGG branch has probability $\frac{1}{2} \times \frac{1}{2} = \frac{1}{4}$, while the GGGBG branch has probability $\frac{1}{2} \times \frac{1}{2} \times \frac{1}{2} = \frac{1}{8}$.

A Baseball Series

Mathematical Goal

- To analyze a binomial situation with multiple-stage outcomes

Launch

Tell the class about the baseball series between the Bobcats and the Gazelles.

- *What is the probability of the series ending in four games? five games? six games? seven games?*
- *Who has the greater chance of winning: the Bobcats or the Gazelles?*

Some students may suggest tossing a coin since it represents a 50% chance of heads or tails. Toss a coin five times to get an example of what could happen. For example, GG <u>GBBBG</u>. Ask:

- *Who wins the series?*
- *How long was the series?*
- *How many different ways could the remaining five games play out?*

Students may begin to see that this is just like the last problem. These are both binomial situations.

Pick a few of the B/G combinations and help the class interpret them in terms of a baseball series. They need to know how long the series went and which team has the greater probability of winning.

Let the class work in pairs.

Explore

Make sure everyone is analyzing the data correctly and has a valid recording scheme.

Summarize

Students will be surprised that the probability of the series ending in four, five, six, or seven games is the same, $\frac{1}{4}$ or $\frac{8}{32}$. But, the Gazelles have a greater chance of winning the series.

If the Gazelles win games 3 and 4, some students may wonder why you have to count all the possibilities for the remaining five games, even those that result in the series ending before all five games are necessary. See the longer discussion of this in the Summarize section.

Materials
- Student notebooks

ACE Assignment Guide
for Problem 4.3

Core 10
Other *Connections* 14–17; unassigned choices from previous problems

Adapted For suggestions about adapting ACE exercises, see the CMP *Special Needs Handbook*.
Connecting to Prior Units 16: *Accentuate the Negative*

Answers to Problem 4.3

A. Answers may vary. In general, students' answers tend toward five or six games.

B. The table below is one of many ways to organize the possibilities. The length of each series is in parentheses. The bold outcomes indicate series won by the Gazelles. The regular outcomes indicate series won by the Bobcats.

C. 1.

Number of Bobcats Wins	Possible Outcomes
5	BBBBB (6)
4	BBBBG (6), BBBGB (7), BBGBB (7), BGBBB (7), GBBBB (7)
3	BBBGG (7), BBGBG (7), BBGGB (6), BGBBG (7), BGBGB (6), BGGBB (5), GBBBG (7), GBBGB (6), GBGBB (5), GGBBB (4)
2	BBGGG (6), BGBGG (6), BGGBG (5), BGGGB (5), GBBGG (6), GBGBG (5), GBGGB (5), GGBBG (4), GGBGB (4), GGGBB (4)
1	GGGGB (4), GGGBG (4), GGBGG (4), GBGGG (5), BGGGG (5)
0	GGGGG (4)

2. P(series ends in four games) $= \frac{8}{32}$

P(series ends in five games) $= \frac{8}{32}$

P(series ends in six games) $= \frac{8}{32}$

P(series ends in seven games) $= \frac{8}{32}$

D. P(Gazelles win the series) $= \frac{26}{32}$;

P(Bobcats win the series) $= \frac{6}{32}$

The student edition pages for this investigation begin on the next page.

Notes _____
_____
_____
_____

Binomial Outcomes

4.1 Guessing Answers

Have you ever forgotten to study for a quiz and had to guess at the answers? If you take a true/false quiz and guess on every question, what are your chances of getting every question right?

Problem 4.1 Finding More Expected Values

A quiz has four true/false questions. Each question is worth 25 points.

- On a piece of paper, write the numbers 1 to 4 to represent the questions for the quiz.
- Toss a penny to determine the answer for each quiz item. Next to each number, write true (T) if a head shows and false (F) if a tail shows.
- After you have written your answers, your teacher will give you the correct answers.
- Mark your answers correct or incorrect. Record your score.

A. Compare answers with your classmates. How many papers had

   1. exactly 4 correct (all correct)

   2. exactly 3 correct (3 correct and 1 incorrect)

Notes _____

_____

_____

_____

3. exactly 2 correct (2 correct and 2 incorrect)

4. exactly 1 correct (1 correct and 3 incorrect)

5. none correct (0 correct and 4 incorrect)

B. 1. If you guess on every question, how many different ways can you get exactly 1 incorrect answer? Exactly 2 incorrect answers? Exactly 3 incorrect answers? All 4 incorrect? All 4 correct?

2. What is the probability of getting

   a. a score of 100 (all correct)

   b. a score of 75 (exactly three correct)

   c. a score of 50 (exactly two correct)

   d. a score of 25 (exactly one correct)

   e. a score of 0 (all incorrect)

C. 1. Suppose you take the quiz 32 times. How many times do you expect to get the given number of correct answers?

   a. 4   **b.** 3   **c.** 2   **d.** 1   **e.** 0

2. What would your total score be in each case?

3. If you take the quiz 32 times, what is the expected average score? Will the expected value change if you take the quiz 100 times? Explain.

D. Suppose the true/false quiz has five questions and you guess each one. What is the probability that you will get them all correct?

ACE Homework starts on page 54.

4.2 Ortonville

Situations like tossing a coin (or the true/false quiz) that have exactly two outcomes are binomial situations. The probability of getting one of two outcomes (like heads or tails) is called a **binomial probability.** In this problem, you will explore another binomial situation that has equally likely outcomes.

Notes _____

_____

_____

_____

Ortonville is a very special town. Each family is named Orton and has exactly five children. The parents in Ortonville have agreed to call their children these names:

The Orton Children

	Girl	Boy
First-Born Child	Gloria	Benson
Second-Born Child	Gilda	Berndt
Third-Born Child	Gail	Blair
Fourth-Born Child	Gerry	Blake
Fifth-Born Child	Gina	Brett

A. List all the possible outcomes for a family with five children.

B. What is the probability that a family has children named Gloria, Gilda, Blair, Blake, and Gina?

C. Find the probability that a family has

  1. exactly five girls or five boys

  2. two girls and three boys

  3. the first or last child a boy

  4. at least one boy

  5. at most one boy

ACE **Homework starts on page 54.**

4.3 A Baseball Series

Every fall the best baseball team in the American League plays the best team in the National League. The series has up to seven games. The first team to win four games wins the series.

Notes _____

_____

_____

_____

Problem 4.3 Expanding Binomial Probability

Suppose the Bobcats are playing the Gazelles in your town's little league "world series." The teams enter the series evenly matched. That is, they each have an equally likely chance of winning each game.

The Gazelles win the first two games of the series. The owner of the concession stands must predict how much food to order for the rest of the series. He needs to know the probability that the series will end in 4, 5, 6, or 7 games. To find the answer, he must find all the possible outcomes.

Label the outcomes with a G for a Gazelles win or a B for a Bobcats win. For example, BBGG means that the Bobcats win the third and fourth games and the Gazelles win the fifth and sixth games. In this example, the series ends in six games, when the Gazelles have won four games. Write G-6 after BBGG.

A. Before you analyze the rest of the series, predict whether it is more probable that the series will end in 4, 5, 6, or 7 games.

B. Suppose all five remaining games are played. What are all of the possible outcomes for these five games?

C. 1. For each outcome, determine the length of the series.

    2. What is the probability that the series ends in four games? Five games? Six games? Seven games?

D. Analyze the outcomes in Question C for wins. What is the probability that the Gazelles win the series? That the Bobcats win the series?

ACE **Homework starts on page 54.**

Did You Know?

The World Series started in 1903 as a best-of-nine-game series. From 1905 until 1919, the series changed to the best-of-seven games. After World War I ended, the series temporarily changed back to the best-of-nine games in 1919–1921. From 1922 until now, the series has remained a best-of-seven-game series. Between 1922 and 2003, the World Series ended in four games and five games both 15 times. It ended in six games 17 times and in seven games 34 times. There was no World Series in 1994.

Go Online
PHSchool.com **For:** Information about the World Series
  Web Code: ane-9031

Investigation 4 Binomial Outcomes   **53**

STUDENT PAGE

STUDENT PAGE

Notes

Applications

1. It costs six tickets to play the Toss-a-Penny game at the school carnival. For each turn, a player tosses a penny three times. If the penny lands heads up two or more times in a turn, the player wins ten tickets to spend on food and games.

   a. Suppose Benito plays the game 80 times. How many tickets can he expect to win?

   b. What is the average number of tickets Benito can expect to win or lose per turn?

2. **a.** If you toss three coins at the same time, is the probability of getting three heads the same as or different from the probability of getting three heads when you toss one coin three times in a row? Explain your reasoning.

   b. If you toss three coins and get three tails, what is the probability you will get three tails when you toss the three coins again? Explain.

For Exercises 3–9, use this information: Scout, Ms. Rodriguez's dog, is about to have puppies. The vet thinks Scout will have four puppies. Assume that for each puppy, a male and female are equally likely.

3. **a.** List all the possible combinations of female and male puppies Scout might have.

   b. Is Scout more likely to have four male puppies or two male and two female puppies? Explain.

4. **Multiple Choice** What is the probability that Scout will have four female puppies?

   A. $\frac{1}{2}$ **B.** $\frac{1}{4}$ **C.** $\frac{1}{8}$ **D.** $\frac{1}{16}$

5. **Multiple Choice** What is the probability that Scout will have two male and two female puppies?

   F. $\frac{1}{2}$ **G.** $\frac{1}{4}$ **H.** $\frac{1}{8}$ **J.** $\frac{6}{16}$

6. **Multiple Choice** What is the probability that Scout will have at least one male puppy?

   A. $\frac{15}{16}$ **B.** $\frac{7}{8}$ **C.** $\frac{3}{4}$ **D.** $\frac{1}{2}$

STUDENT PAGE

STUDENT PAGE

Notes _____

_____

_____

_____

7. Multiple Choice What is the probability that Scout will have at least one female puppy?

F. $\frac{15}{16}$ **G.** $\frac{7}{8}$ **H.** $\frac{3}{4}$ **J.** $\frac{1}{2}$

8. Ms. Rodriguez plans to sell her dog's female puppies for $250 each and her male puppies for $200 each. How much money can she expect to make from a litter of four puppies?

9. Suppose the vet thinks Scout will have a litter of five puppies. How much money can Ms. Rodriguez expect to make from selling the puppies?

10. Rajan's class is holding a world series. They divide the class into two teams, which are evenly matched. One team is the Champs and the other team is the Stars. The series is five games, and the first team to win three games wins the series. The Champs win the first game.

    a. What is the probability that the series will end in 3, 4, or 5 games?

    b. What is the probability that the Stars will win the series?

Connections

11. You might find that a tree diagram is a helpful model in this exercise.

    a. What are all the possible outcomes when you toss a coin three times?

    b. How many outcomes are there when you toss a coin four times? (You do not have to list them all.) Five times?

    c. How many ways can you get five heads in five tosses? How many ways can you get zero heads in five tosses? How many ways can you get four heads? One head? Three heads? Two heads?

    d. Explain why some symmetry in your answers in part (c) makes sense.

Go Online
PHSchool.com
For: Multiple-Choice Skills Practice
Web Code: ana-7454

Investigation 4 Binomial Outcomes   **55**

Notes _____

_____

_____

_____

12. The largest hamster litter on record consisted of 26 babies. Suppose a hamster has 26 babies. Assume that the birth of a female and the birth of a male are equally likely. What is the theoretical probability that all 26 babies will be male? Explain your reasoning.

Homework Help nline
PHSchool.com
For: Help with Exercise 12
Web Code: ane-7412

13. In the unit *How Likely Is It?*, you learned about genetics. Every person has a combination of two tongue-curling alleles, TT, Tt, or tt, where T is the dominant tongue-curling allele, and t is the recessive non-tongue-curling allele. A person with at least one T allele will be able to curl his or her tongue.

Kent found out that his tongue-curling alleles are tt and his wife Diane's alleles are Tt. He makes this table to help him determine the possible outcomes for their children.

	Kent	
	t	t
T	Tt	Tt
t	tt	tt

Diane

The possible combinations are Tt, Tt, tt, and tt. This means that a child of Kent and Diane has a 50% chance of being able to curl his or her tongue.

a. Suppose Kent and Diane have two children. What is the probability that both of the children will be able to curl their tongues? Make a tree diagram to help you answer this question.

b. Suppose Kent and Diane have four children. What is the probability that none of the children will be able to curl their tongues?

c. Suppose Kent and Diane have four children. What is the probability that only the oldest child will be able to curl his or her tongue?

Notes _____

_____

_____

_____

14. King George's home, Castle Warwick, is under siege. King George must escape to his cousin's home, Castle Howard. The only escape route is through a series of canals, shown below.

There are five gates in the series of canals. Each gate opens and closes at random and is open half the time and closed the other half. The arrows show the way the water is flowing.

Castle Warwick

Castle Howard

a. What is the probability that a water route from Castle Warwick to Castle Howard is open?

b. How is this exercise similar to Problem 4.3?

15. Drew, the paper carrier, collects $10 per week from each customer for the paper. One customer offers him these deals.

a. Toss five coins. If there are four or more heads, the customer pays $18. Otherwise, he pays $4. Find the expected value for this deal. Decide if it is a fair deal.

b. Toss five coins. If they are all the same, the customer pays $80. Otherwise, he pays $4. Find the expected value for this deal. Decide if it is a fair deal.

Notes _____

_____

_____

_____

16. Ethan makes a game played on the number line. At the start of a turn, a player places a marker on 0. The player tosses a penny and moves the marker one unit to the right if the penny lands heads up and one unit to the left if it lands tails up. A turn is three tosses, and the score for that turn is the number naming the location of the marker at the end of that turn.

a. What scores are possible after one turn (three tosses)?

b. Suppose Ethan changes his game so that a turn consists of four tosses. What scores would be possible after one turn?

17. a. Spinning the pointer at the right once makes a binomial situation. What are the possible outcomes of a single spin? What is the probability of each outcome?

b. Spinning the spinner from part (a) three times is also a binomial situation. If the result of the first spin is Red, does this affect the possible outcomes of the second and third spins? What is the probability of RBB (in this order), assuming each spin is independent of the previous spin?

c. Using the spinner at the right once is *not* a binomial situation. What are the possible outcomes? What is the probability of each?

d. Does spinning the spinner at the right make a binomial situation? Explain.

e. Suppose you spin the spinner in part (d) three times. What is the probability of RBB (in this order)?

58   What Do You Expect?

Notes _____

_____

_____

_____

Extensions

Pascal's Triangle (on the left, below) can be used to summarize binomial probabilities and answer new questions in some binomial situations. The sum of each row is the same as the number of outcomes in a binomial probability. For example, some binomial situations are written across from their corresponding row.

Pascal's Triangle						Coin	True/False Test
		1					
	1		1			Tossing 1 coin	1 question
	1	2		1		Tossing 2 coins	2 questions
1	3		3		1	Tossing 3 coins	3 questions
1	4	6	4		1	Tossing 4 coins	4 questions
1	5	10	10	5	1	Tossing 5 coins	5 questions

18. Describe some patterns in Pascal's Triangle.

19. What is the sixth row (the next row in the diagram above) of Pascal's Triangle? Describe what probabilities each number represents in a situation that involves tossing 6 coins.

In your answers for Exercises 20–22, tell which row from Pascal's Triangle you used.

20. On a five-question true/false test, what is the probability that you will guess exactly two correct answers?

21. A coin is tossed six times. What is the probability that at least two heads occur?

22. On a nine-question true/false test, what is the probability that you will guess exactly three correct answers?

Investigation 4 Binomial Outcomes   **59**

Notes _____

_____

_____

_____

Mathematical Reflections 4

In this investigation, you looked at probabilities for situations involving a series of actions, each with two equally likely outcomes. The following questions will help you summarize what you have learned.

Think about your answers to these questions. Discuss your ideas with other students and your teacher. Then write a summary of your findings in your notebook.

1. Describe five different binomial situations. Explain why they are binomial situations.

2. Tossing a coin three times is an example of a situation involving a series of three actions, each with two equally likely outcomes.

   a. Pick one of the situations you described in Question 1. Describe a series of three actions, each with two equally likely outcomes. Make a list of all the possible outcomes.

   b. Write a question about your situation that can be answered by your list.

3. As you increase the number of actions for a binomial situation, what happens to the total number of possible outcomes? For example, if you increase the number of times a coin is tossed, what happens to the total number of outcomes?

Notes _____

_____

_____

_____

Investigation

ACE
Assignment Choices

Differentiated Instruction
Solutions for All Learners

Problem 4.1

Core 11
Other *Applications* 1, 2

Problem 4.2

Core 3–8
Other *Applications* 9, *Connections* 12–13; *Extensions* 18–22; unassigned choices from previous problems

Problem 4.3

Core 10
Other *Connections* 14–17; unassigned choices from previous problems

Adapted For suggestions about adapting ACE exercises, see the CMP *Special Needs Handbook*.
Connecting to Prior Units 11: *How Likely Is It?*; 16: *Accentuate the Negative*

Applications

1. **a.** As shown in the tree diagram below, Benito can toss two or more heads in four ways (indicated with an asterisk below), a $\frac{4}{8}$ probability of winning. To play, Benito would pay 80 × 6 = 480 tickets. Since he could expect to win 40 times, he would win 40 × 10 = 400 tickets. So he would have an expected loss of 80 tickets.

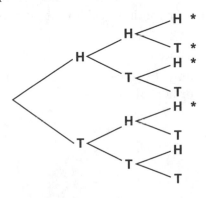

b. Benito can expect to lose 80 ÷ 80 = 1 ticket per turn.

2. **a.** The probabilities would be the same, provided all the coins are fair.

   b. The probability of getting three tails will always be $\frac{1}{8}$. The previous toss is irrelevant. Coins do not remember what happened on previous tosses. Students might list the possibilities in a tree diagram or an organized list.

3. **a.** Students might list the possibilities in a tree diagram or an organized list.

Number of Males	Possible Outcomes
4	MMMM
3	MMMF, MMFM, MFMM, FMMM
2	MMFF, MFMF, MFFM, FMMF, FMFM, FFMM
1	MFFF, FMFF, FFMF, FFFM
0	FFFF

b. The probability of four male puppies is 1 out of 16, or $\frac{1}{16}$. The probability of two male and two female puppies is 6 out of 16, or $\frac{6}{16}$. Scout is much more likely to have two male and two female puppies.

4. D   5. J   6. A   7. F

8. Because a male and a female are equally likely outcomes for each puppy in the litter, there is an expected value of $\frac{1}{2} \times \$250 + \frac{1}{2} \times \$200 = \$225$ for each puppy. Ms. Rodriguez can expect to make 4($225) = $900 on a litter of four puppies. (Note: Another way to analyze the problem is to make a list of the possible outcomes and look at the money that Ms. Rodriguez would make in each case. Then take the average of these amounts. The results are the same either way.)

9. Except for the number of puppies, this solution uses the same numbers as Exercise 8. $\frac{1}{2} \times \$250 + \frac{1}{2} \times \$200 = \$225$ for each puppy. Ms. Rodriguez can expect to make $5(\$225) = \$1,125$ on a litter of five puppies.

10. a. $P(3 \text{ games}) = \frac{1}{4}$, $P(4 \text{ games}) = \frac{3}{8}$, and $P(5 \text{ games}) = \frac{3}{8}$. Students may make a table like the one below. A tree diagram can also be used.

CCCC (C-3)	CCCS (C-3)	CCSS (C-3)	SSSC (S-4)	SSSS (S-4)
	CCSC (C-3)	CSCS (C-4)	SCSS (S-5)	
	CSCC (C-4)	CSSC (C-5)	SSCS (S-5)	
	SCCC (C-4)	SCCS (C-4)	CSSS (S-5)	
		SCSC (C-5)		
		SSCC (C-5)		

b. From the table above, P(Stars win) $= \frac{5}{16}$.

Connections

11. You might find a tree diagram is a helpful model in this exercise.

 a. HHH, HHT, HTH, THH, HTT, THT, TTH, TTT

 b. 16 outcomes for 4 tosses and 32 for 5 tosses. Students can see from the tree model made for part (a) that adding another toss makes two more choices of ways to end the prior list, so twice as long a list.

 c. HHHHH only happens one way. TTTTT only happens one way. HHHHT, HHHTH, HHTHH, HTHHH, THHHH are five ways to get four heads. There are also five ways to get one head. HHHTT, HHTHT, HHTTH, HTHHT, HTHTH, HTTHH, THHHT, THHTH, THTHH, TTHHH are ten ways to get three heads.

 There are also ten ways to get two heads.

d. It makes sense that if two outcomes A and B are equally likely, then the probability of AAAAA is the same as the probability of BBBBB. Likewise, the probability of four A's is the same as the probability of four B's, which is the same as getting only one A. And the probability of three A's is the same as the probability of three B's, which is the same as getting two As.

12. Students may have realized by now that each time they add a branch to a tree diagram, they are multiplying. For example, with 4 babies, there are $2 \times 2 \times 2 \times 2 = 16$ possible outcomes. With 5 babies, there are $2 \times 2 \times 2 \times 2 \times 2 = 32$ outcomes. So, for 26 babies, there are $2 \times 2 \times 2 \times \ldots \times 2 = 2^{26} = 67,108,864$ outcomes. (Note: If students have not yet studied exponents, don't expect them to use this notation.)

 Having all males would be only one of these outcomes, so $P(26 \text{ males}) = \frac{1}{67,108,864}$.

13. a. As shown in the tree diagram below, there are four possible outcomes, and only one is that both children can curl their tongues, with a probability of $\frac{1}{4}$.

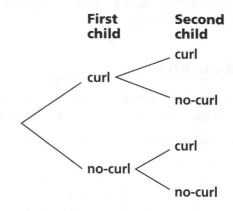

 b. There is a 1 in 16, or $\frac{1}{16}$, probability that all four children will not be able to curl their tongues.

 c. There is a 1 in 16, or $\frac{1}{16}$, probability that only the oldest child will be able to curl his or her tongue.

14. a. The probability that a water route is open is $\frac{19}{32}$. In Figure 2, C represents that the gate is closed and O that the gate is open. An N is used to indicate that there is no possible way for King George to escape and Y indicates that there is a way to escape. The gates 1–5 are in order; for example, CCOCO means that gates 1, 2, and 4 are closed and gates 3 and 5 are open.

b. They each deal with binomial situations. Also, they each have 32 possible outcomes.

15. a. Since $P(4 \text{ or } 5 \text{ heads}) = \frac{6}{32}$, in 32 weeks Drew can expect to get $18 six times and $4 twenty-six times $(32 - 6 = 26)$. So the expected value is $(6 \times \$18) + (26 \times \$4) = \$212$. Drew will only get $\$212 \div 32 = \$6.63$ per week. This offer is unfair.

b. Since $P(\text{all same}) = \frac{2}{32}$, in 32 weeks Drew can expect to get $80 two times and $4 thirty times. So the expected value is $(2 \times \$80) + (30 \times \$4) = \$280$. Drew will only get $\$280 \div 32 = \$8.75$ per week. This offer is unfair.

16. a. The tree diagram shows that with the three tosses, the possible scores are: $-3, -1, 1,$ and 3.

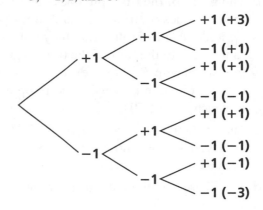

b. The possible scores for four tosses are $-4, -2, 0, 2,$ and 4. (Note: Students may need to construct a tree diagram to see this, or they may start to draw conclusions after experimenting with the game and checking their results after several trials.)

Figure 2

CCCCC (N)	CCCCO (N)	CCCOO (Y)	CCOOO (Y)	COOOO (Y)	OOOOO (Y)
	CCCOC (N)	CCOCO (N)	COOOC (Y)	OCOOO (Y)	
	CCOCC (N)	CCOOC (N)	OOOCC (Y)	OOCOO (Y)	
	COCCC (N)	COOCC (Y)	COCOO (Y)	OOOCO (Y)	
	OCCCC (N)	COCOC (N)	COOCO (Y)	OOOOC (Y)	
		COCCO (N)	OCOOC (Y)		
		OOCCC (N)	OOCOC (Y)		
		OCOCC (Y)	OOCCO (N)		
		OCCOC (Y)	OCCOO (Y)		
		OCCCO (N)	OCOCO (Y)		

17. a. The outcomes are R, with a probability of 25%, and B, with a probability of 75%.

b. The result of the first spin does not affect the outcomes of the second and third spins. $\frac{9}{64}$; students may realize that they only need to investigate the part of the tree diagram that starts with R. If they draw this part of the tree diagram they will have 16 options, of which 9 are RBB.

c. The probability of R is 25%, of Y is 25%, and of B is 50%. This is not a binomial setting because there are more than two outcomes.

d. Yes. There are two outcomes for each spin.

e. $\frac{4}{27}$

Extensions

18. Possible answers: There are ones along the outside of the triangle. When you add the two numbers above a number, the sum is that number. For example, the 3 in the third row is $1 + 2$, which are the numbers above the 3.

19. The sixth row (not counting the row with just 1 as a row) of Pascal's triangle is: 1, 6, 15, 20, 15, 6, 1. The sixth row states that there is 1 way to get six heads, 6 ways to get five heads and one tail, 15 ways to get four heads and two tails, 20 ways to get three heads and three tails, 15 ways to get two heads and four tails, 6 ways to get one head and five tails, and 1 way to get six tails.

20. $P(2 \text{ correct}) = \frac{10}{32}$. Use row 5.

21. $P(\text{at least 2 heads}) = \frac{57}{64}$. Students may find this probability directly by adding $1 + 6 + 15 + 20 + 15 = 57$ out of the total 64 outcomes, or some students may find $P(1 \text{ or no heads}) = \frac{7}{64}$ and subtract this from one, giving $1 - (\frac{7}{64}) = \frac{57}{64}$. Use row 6.

22. $P(\text{exactly 3 correct}) = \frac{84}{512} = \frac{21}{128}$. Use row 9.

Possible Answers to Mathematical Reflections

1. Possible answers: tossing a coin, rolling a number cube for an odd or even number, spinning a spinner that is half blue and half white, choosing colored blocks or marbles from a bag that contains half of one color and half of another, and choosing red or black cards from a 52-card deck. These are binomial situations because there are only two possible outcomes.

2. a. Possible answer: tossing a coin three times or three coins:

TTT	HTT
TTH	HTH
THT	HHT
THH	HHH

b. What is the probability that all coins are the same? What is the probability that there are exactly three heads?

3. As the number of actions increases, the total number of possible outcomes doubles. For example, if 2 coins are tossed, there would be 4 outcomes; if 3 coins are tossed, there would be 8 outcomes; if 4 coins are tossed, there would be 16 outcomes; and for 5 coins there are 32 outcomes, etc. If a tree diagram is made for outcomes on a four-item true/false quiz, then one can just as easily be made for tossing coins or the gender of children by replacing *question* with *coin*, or *child*, etc.

Answers to Looking Back and Looking Ahead

1. a. Possible answer:

b. Possible answer:

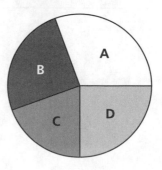

c. i. $\frac{1}{4}$ **ii.** $\frac{3}{4}$ **iii.** $\frac{7}{10}$

2. a.

b. $\frac{1}{4}$ **c.** $\frac{3}{4}$

d–e. This is not a fair game because Jim has a 75% chance of not getting a match, and Gabrielle has only a 25% chance of getting a match. It could be made fair by readjusting the point scheme. For example, 3 points for a match and 1 point for a no-match is fair.

3. a. He should expect 3 wins for a total of 12 points, 9 losses for a total loss of 18 points. Altogether, he should expect to lose 6 points.

b. $-\frac{1}{2}$ (a loss of $\frac{1}{2}$ point)

c. This game is not fair because the player loses a little bit on an average turn. One way to make it fair is to award 3 points for a win and take away 1 point for a loss.

4. The fractions tell us that over a large number of trials, the desired outcome will occur about 1 out of 2 times or 2 out of 3 times or 5 out of 8 times. Generally, these fractions can be converted to percents, and thus the event will occur about 50%, or $66\frac{2}{3}$%, or 62.5% of the time. These are mathematical predictions based upon the available information about a situation. The actual outcomes will be close to these predictions if the number of trials is large enough.

5. As the number of trials increases, the experimental probability approaches the theoretical probability. For a small number of trials, the experimental and theoretical probabilities for a given event are likely to differ.

6. a. Tree diagrams offer a method to find all the possible outcomes of a situation. Student examples will vary. One example of using a tree diagram is to find out the outcomes of spinning two spinners, as in the Making Purple game in Problem 2.1.

b. Area models are useful in making a visual representation of the likelihood of each of the possible outcomes. They show what part of the whole each possible outcome represents. Student examples will vary. One example of using an area model was in Problem 3.1, when students were trying to figure out how many times Nicky would score 0, 1, or 2 points in a one-and-one free-throw situation.

7. The expected value or long-term average is the average payoff over many trials. To determine expected value, first determine the possible outcomes and the related theoretical probabilities. Once the theoretical probabilities are known, multiply the number of trials to be completed by each of these probabilities to determine the expected values for the given situation. For example, suppose you are playing a game with two coins in which you score 2 points if the toss is at least one head and 1 point if the toss is two tails. The theoretical probability of getting a head is $\frac{3}{4}$ (HH, TH, or HT) and of getting two tails is $\frac{1}{4}$ (TT). If you toss the two coins 36 times, then you would expect to get a head 27 times out of the 36 tosses and two tails 9 times out of 36 tosses. Therefore, the expected value is $\frac{3}{4} \times 2 + \frac{1}{4} \times 1$, which is $\frac{7}{4}$ or $1\frac{3}{4}$. You expect to score about $1\frac{3}{4}$ points per toss of the coins. Expected value was computed for the points Nicky would score in a one-and-one free-throw situation in Problem 3.2 and in Problem 3.3, where students decided how much money Julie and Li Fong would receive from different payment plans.

Assigning the Unit Project

The optional Unit Project offers an opportunity for students to apply the probability concepts they have studied, including expected value, in a real-world context. Students are asked to design a new game for a school carnival or to redesign one of the games that was studied in this unit. In testing their games and writing a report about them, students will need to collect, organize, and analyze data.

This section contains preparation notes for the Carnival Game project and a holistic-by-category scoring rubric with guidelines for using the rubric to assess the project. Samples of one group's project, along with reports from two students, and a teacher's comments accompany the suggested rubric.

Preparing for the Carnival Game Project

This project works well with groups of three or four. Some teachers have groups work together to design and make models of their game and to discuss the report, and then have students write their final reports individually.

Students will need access to commonly available mathematics materials such as calculators, rulers, compasses, number cubes, coins, spinners, blocks, and counters. In addition, students will need materials such as cardboard, construction paper, tape, and markers to construct their models.

The project may be launched near the end of the unit, sometime after Investigation 3. The project will require several hours to complete, though most of this work could be done outside of class. You may want to take half a class period to get students started. Have them form groups, review the project handout, then brainstorm their game design. For the next few days, you might reserve the last ten minutes of class for groups to meet, report to each other, get advice from others in the class or from you, and do whatever else they need to do to make progress on their projects.

Some teachers have groups share their game with the class as part of their final report. Others have expanded the project into a school event in which groups set up their games in the gymnasium and students from other grades come to the Math Carnival and play the games (using tokens rather than money).

Grading the Unit Project

A possible scoring rubric and two sample projects with teacher comments follow.

Suggested Scoring Rubric

This rubric employs a point scale for two separate areas of assessment for a total of 22 points. Use the rubric as presented here, or modify it to fit your needs and your district's requirements for evaluating and reporting students' work and understanding.

Game Design

Rules for the game (0–3 points)

3 COMPLETE RESPONSE

Rules for the game are clear, complete, and address how to play the game, how to win the game, how much the game costs to play, and how much a player wins.

2 REASONABLY COMPLETE RESPONSE

Rules for the game are clear but incomplete. One of the following is missing: how to play the game, how to win the game, how much the game costs to play, or how much a player wins.

1 PARTIAL RESPONSE

Rules do not address at least two of the following: how to play the game, how to win the game, how much the game costs to play, or how much a player wins.

0 INADEQUATE RESPONSE

Rules are not included or cannot be followed.

Scale model or model (0–2 points)

2 COMPLETE RESPONSE

Model is a neat and accurate representation of the game. If it is a scale model, the scale factor from it to the actual game is given.

1 PARTIAL RESPONSE

Model is included but does not match the description given.

0 INADEQUATE OR NO RESPONSE

Model is not included.

Profit (0–2 points)

2 COMPLETE RESPONSE

Group correctly concludes that the game would make a profit and explains why.

1 PARTIAL RESPONSE

Group correctly concludes that the game would make a profit but does not explain why.

0 INADEQUATE OR NO RESPONSE

Group does not address profit or the game does not make a profit.

Ease of use (0–1 point)

1 COMPLETE RESPONSE

The game is easy to use.

0 INADEQUATE OR NO RESPOINSE

The game is not easy to use.

Ease of construction (0–1 point)

1 COMPLETE RESPONSE

The game is easy to construct.

0 INADEQUATE RESPONSE

The game is not easy to construct.

Written Report
Probability of winning (0–3 points)

3 COMPLETE RESPONSE

Student correctly gives the theoretical probability of winning the game and correctly finds the experimental probability from playing the game and resolves any difference between the two probabilities. Or, student offers an adequate explanation of why the theoretical probability for the game cannot be found and performs a substantial number (depending on the complexity of the game) of trials of the game and correctly finds the experimental probability based on these data.

2 REASONABLY COMPLETE RESPONSE

Student has made a small error or errors and only the theoretical probability (or a reason why it cannot be found) or only the experimental probability is correct. Or, student offers an adequate explanation of why the theoretical probability cannot be found but the number of trials is insufficient to draw conclusions even though the experimental probability may be correct based on the limited data.

1 PARTIAL RESPONSE

One of the probabilities, experimental or theoretical, is not addressed correctly.

0 INADEQUATE RESPONSE

Neither experimental probability nor theoretical probability is addressed correctly.

Expected payout (0–3 points)

3 COMPLETE RESPONSE

Student gives the correct expected payout and enough information for the reader to understand how it was calculated.

2 REASONABLY COMPLETE RESPONSE

Student gives the correct expected payout but does not give enough information for the reader to understand how it was calculated. Or, student has made a small error in calculating the expected payout but does give enough information for the reader to understand how it was calculated.

1 PARTIAL RESPONSE

Student has made an error in calculating the expected payout and does not give enough information for the reader to understand how it was calculated.

0 NO RESPONSE

No expected payout is given.

Data collection (0–2 points)

2 COMPLETE RESPONSE

Student describes data collection, gives results, and connects this information to the probability of winning the game or the expected payout.

1 PARTIAL RESPONSE

Student describes data collection and gives results but does not connect this information to the probability of winning the game or the expected payout.

0 INADEQUATE OR NO RESPONSE

Student does not describe data collection or give results.

Explanation for why the game should be in the carnival (0–2 points)

2 COMPLETE RESPONSE

Student addresses why people will want to play the game (and says more than "they will like it") and why it should be in the carnival.

1 PARTIAL RESPONSE

Student addresses why people will want to play the game or why it should be in the carnival, but not both.

0 INADEQUATE OR NO RESPONSE

These ideas are not addressed.

Overall flow, organization, and presentation (0–3 points)

3 COMPLETE RESPONSE

Report is clearly stated, easy to follow, and neatly presented.

2 REASONABLY COMPLETE RESPONSE

Report is neatly presented and, with some effort, the reader can follow it.

1 PARTIAL RESPONSE

Report is not neatly presented and effort is needed by the reader to follow it.

0 INADEQUATE RESPONSE

Report is unacceptable.

Sample Student Work

Below is a Carnival Game project presented by one group of students. In this classroom, students worked on the project in groups of four, and each member of the group wrote his or her own report. Following the project are two individual reports written by students in the group and a teacher's explanation of how the reports were scored using the suggested rubric.

Spin-Loser-Draw

HOW TO PLAY

This game costs $0.25 to play. The operator will hold a bucket filled with colored cubes. He/she will hold it above the players head so he/she can not see. The player then chooses one colored cube from the bucket without looking. The player must remember the color of the block and make sure that the operator knows the color of the cube also. Then you will replace the colored cube back into the bucket. Then the operator will spin the spinner. If the color that the spinner lands on matches the color of the cube that you drew, then you are a winner! You will earn a prize bases on the color of the match that you got. (See prize list).

OBJECT

The object of this game is to have the spinner match the color of block that you have drawn from the bucket.

RULES

1. Must pay $0.25 to play Spin-loser-draw.
2. Pick one cube per game only.
3. Do not look at the cubes while drawing.
4. Operator must spin spinner.
5. Colors on spinner and cube must match to win

Spin-Loser-Draw Prize List

If you match two....Greens....you get......$0.50

If you match two....Oranges..you get......$0.75

If you match two....Blues......you get......$0.75

If you match two....Yellows...you get......$1.00

If you match two....Polka-dots you get.$1.00

If you match two....Reds......you get......$1.00

If you match two....Stars......you get......$2.00

If you match two....Plaids...you get......$2.00

Susy's Written Report

Susy

Dear Carnival Commite,

We are submiting a game for the school carnival. Our game is fun, easy, and profitable. We think our game should be in the carnival becase it will be fun for people to play. It's not very expensive to play and it could be an easy game to make money off of. We believe that a lot of people will keep playing so they can win more money, or get their money back.

Following is the probability of winning the game, first of each pattern and then all together.

Also we found how much profit we would make with our experimental data. For 100 games the total amont taking in is $25.⁰⁰. We figured how much money we had to payout, depending on the number of wins for each catigory. Below is are figuring.

Pattern	Wins	$ out
Star		
Plaid		
Polka-dot	11	2.00
Blue	‖‖	3.75
Red		
Green	lll	1.50
Orange	‖‖	3.75

Total taken in = $25.

Payouts = $11.

Profit = $14.

Pattern	Chances of Winning	Pattern	Chances of Winning
Star	$\frac{1}{324}$	Blue	$\frac{9}{324}$
Plaid	$\frac{1}{324}$	Orange	$\frac{9}{324}$
Yellow	$\frac{4}{324}$	Polka-dot	$\frac{4}{324}$
Red	$\frac{4}{324}$	Green	$\frac{16}{324}$

Total amount of chances of winning is $\frac{48}{324}$.

We have also tested our game. Here are our results of 100 trials:

Star- 0/100   Blue- 5/100
Plaid- 0/100   Red- 0/100
Yellow- 0/100 Orange- 5/100
Green- 3/100   Polka-dot- 2/100

The total winning is 19/100.

Here is the expected value theoretically. The values are out of 324.

Star	2.⁰⁰	Green	2.⁰⁰
Plaid	2.⁰⁰	Red	2.⁰⁰
Polk-dot	2.⁰⁰	Blue	2.²⁵
Yellow	2.⁰⁰	Orange	2.²⁵

$81.⁰⁰ to take in
$16.⁵⁰ to give out
$64.⁵⁰ profit

Thank-you,

Susy

Susy's Data

Top-left panel

Star
Plaid
Yellow 1
Yellow 2
Polka-dot 1
Polka-dot 2
Red 1
Red 2
Orange 1
Orange 2
Orange 3
Blue 1
Blue 2
Blue 3
Green 1
Green 2
Green 3
Green 4
(Star)

Plaid
Star
Yellow 1
Yellow 2
Polka-dot 1
Polka-dot 2
Red 1
Red 2
Orange 1
Orange 2
Orange 3
Blue 1
blue 2
Blue 3
Green 1
Green 2
Green 3
Green 4
(Plaid)

Yellow 1
Plaid
Star
(Yellow 1)
Yellow 2
Polka-dot 1
Polka-dot 2
Red 1
Red 2
Orange 1
Orange 2
Orange 3
Blue 1
Blue 2
Blue 3
Green 1
Green 2
Green 3
Green 4

Yellow 2
Plaid
Star
Yellow 1
(Yellow 2)
Polka-dot 1
Polka-dot 2
Red 1
Red 2
Orange 1
Orange 2
Orange 3
Blue 1
Blue 2
Blue 3
Green 1
Green 2
Green 3
Green 4

Polka-dot 1
Plaid
Star
Yellow 1
Yellow 2
Red 1
Red2
Orange 1
Orange 2
Orange 3
Blue 1
Blue 2
Blue 3
Green 1
Green 2
Green 3
Green 4
(Polka-dot 1)
Polka-dot 2

Polka-dot 2
Plaid
Star
Yellow 1
Yellow 2
Polka-dot 1
(Polka-dot 2)
Red 1
Red 2
Orange 1
Orange 2
Orange 3
Blue 1
Blue 2
Blue 3
Green 1
Green 2
Green 3
Green 4

Top-right panel

Blue 2
Plaid
Star
Polka-dot 1
Polka-dot 2
Red 1
Red 2
Orange 1
Orange 2
Orange 3
Blue 1
(Blue 2)
Blue 3
Green 1
Green 2
Green 3
Green 4

Blue 3
Plaid
Polka-dot 1
Polka-dot 2
Yellow 1
Yellow 2
Red 1
Red 2
Orange 1
Orange 2
Orange 3
Blue 1
Blue 2
(Blue 3)
Green 1
Green 2
Green 3
Green 4

Green 1
Plaid
Star
Polka-dot 1
Polka-dot 2
Yellow 1
Yellow 2
Red 1
Red2
Orange 1
Orange 2
Orange 3
Blue 1
Blue 2
Blue 3
(Green 1)
Green 2
Green 3
Green 4

Green 2
Plaid
Star
Polka-dot 1
Polka-dot 2
Red 1
Red2
Orange 1
Orange 2
Orange 3
Blue 1
Blue 2
Blue 3
Green 1
(Green 2)
Green 3
Green 4

Green 3
Plaid
Star
Polka-dot 1
Polka-dot 2
Yellow 1
Yellow 2
Red 1
Red 2
Orange 1
Orange 2
Orange 3
Blue 1
Blue 2
Blue 3
Green 1
Green 2
(Green 3)
Green 4

Green 4
Plaid
Star
Polka-dot 1
Polka-dot 2
Yellow 1
Yellow 2
Red 1
Red 2
Orange 1
Orange 2
Orange 3
Blue 1
Blue 2
Blue 3
Green 1
Green 2
Green 3
(Green 4)

Bottom-left panel

Red 1
Plaid
Star
Yellow 1
Yellow 2
Polka-dot 1
Polka-dot 2
(Red 1)
Red 2
Orange 1
Orange 2
Orange 3
Blue 1
Blue 2
Blue 3
Green 1
Green 2
Green 3
Green 4

Red 2
Plaid
Star
Polka-dot1
Polka-dot 2
Red 1
(Red 2)
Orange 1
Orange 2
Orange 3
Blue 1
Blue 2
Blue 3
Green 1
Green 2
Green 3
Green 4

Orange 1
Plaid
Star
Yellow 1
Yellow 2
Red 1
Red 2
(Orange 1)
Orange 2
Orange 3
Blue 1
Blue 2
Blue 3
Green 1
Green 2
Green 3
Green 4

Orange 2
Plaid
Star
Yellow 1
Yellow 2
Red 1
Red 2
Polka-dot 1
Polka-dot 2
Orange 1
(Orange 2)
Orange 3
Blue 1
BLue 2
Blue 3
Green 1
Green 2
Green 3
Green 4

Orange 3
Plaid
Star
Polka-dot 1
Polka-dot 2
Red 1
Red 2
Orange 1
Orange 2
(Orange 3)
Blue 1
BLue 2
Blue 3
Green 1
Green 2
Green 3
Green 4

Blue 1
Plaid
Star
Yellow 1
Yellow 2
Polka-dot 1
Polka-dot 2
Red 1
Red 2
Orange 1
Orange 2
Orange 3
(Blue 1)
Blue 2
Blue 3
Green 1
Green 2
Green 3
Green 4

Heidi's Written Report

Heidi

Report: Carnival Game

Dear Carnival Directors;

I would like to introduce a game made for the upcoming carnival. I and three others spent time considering what the kids would enjoy playing, but will give us a profit.

Here's how you play Spin-Loser-draw. We have a bucket containing cubes. The contanents of the bucket are: 4 green cubes, 3 blue and three orange cubes, 2 red, polka-dot and yellow cubes and I star and plaid cube, a total of 18 cubes. For each cube there is 1/18 slot filled in matching it on the spinner. The player draws a

cube without looking from the bucket. Then the game operator spins the spiner. If the spinner matches the drawn cube, the player won! It's that simple.

Kids will want to play for that reason. It appears that it is very simple to win. Two colors, and they're in luck. And, at the low price of only a quarter, they're going to want to try their luck again and again. The prizes also appear very tempting to them.

The prizes are based on the different colors of the match. There are more greens, so there is a better chance that 2 greens will be drawn, so greens are worth less. Where plaids or stars have the least,

and the lowest chance of being drawn, therefor it is worth the most in prize money.

This game has been tested. We played it 100 times. Out of those experimental trys, we won 6 times. So this game will make quite a profit. Out of 100 games, we expect to give out approximatly $11 dollars. But each game cost 25 cents, which is $25 dollars. So we will be making $14.00 profit every 100 games. We calculated all the possible conbimations of cubes and spiner. We added up how many times you could win. Our numbers came out as 48 winning combinations out of 324 total possible.

This is approximetley 5.5 wins in 100 games, which we calculated for experimetal trys.

Please include our game at your carnival. The kids will enjoy it, while you're making a profit

Thanks.

Heidi

Heidi's Data

	Bucket	Spinner	W	L
1.	ORANGE	ORANGE	*	
2.	GREEN	GREEN	*	
3.	BLUE	BLUE	*	
4.	BLUE	ORANGE		*
5.	GREEN	ORANGE		*
6.	BLUE	RED		*
7.	STAR	GREEN		*
8.	STAR	GREEN		*
9.	PLAID	STAR		*
10.	YELLOW	GREEN		*
11.	GREEN	BLUE		*
12.	BLUE	RED		*
13.	ORANGE	BLUE		*
14.	GREEN	ORANGE		*
15.	PLAID	ORANGE		*
16.	ORANGE	POLKA-DOT		*
17.	GREEN	BLUE		*
18.	POLKA-DOT	GREEN		*
19.	ORANGE	POLKA-DOT		*
20.	RED	POLKA-DOT		*
21.	GREEN	GREEN	*	
22.	BLUE	RED		*
23.	GREEN	POLKA-DOT		*
24.	POLKA-DOT	RED		*
25.	POLKA-DOT	POLKA-DOT	*	
26.	BLUE	RED		*
27.	GREEN	GREEN	*	
28.	POLKA-DOT	GREEN		*
29.	RED	ORANGE		*
30.	ORANGE	ORANGE	*	
31.	ORANGE	GREEN		*
32.	BLUE	POLKA-DOT		*

	Bucket	Spinner	W	L
33.	YELLOW	STAR		*
34.	BLUE	RED		*
35.	ORANGE	YELLOW		*
36.	ORANGE	GREEN		*
37.	BLUE	POLKA-DOT		*
38.	RED	YELLOW		*
39.	BLUE	GREEN		*
40.	ORANGE	GREEN		*
41.	ORANGE	ORANGE	*	
42.	RED	POLKA-DOT	*	
43.	POLKA-DOT	GREEN		*
44.	GREEN	POLKA-DOT		*
45.	POLKA-DOT	ORANGE		*
46.	GREEN	ORANGE		*
47.	BLUE	STAR		*
48.	GREEN	PLAID		*
49.	GREEN	ORANGE		*
50.	YELLOW	ORANGE		*
51.	GREEN	PLAID		*
52.	GREEN	ORANGE		*
53.	YELLOW	ORANGE		*
54.	RED	PLAID		*
55.	BLUE	ORANGE		*
56.	PLAID	GREEN		*
57.	ORANGE	ORANGE	*	
58.	GREEN	ORANGE		
59.	POLKA-DOT	GREEN		
60.	GREEN	BLUE		
61.	ORANGE	BLUE		
62.	BLUE	RED		
63.	ORANGE	GREEN		
64.	BLUE	RED		
65.	PLAID	YELLOW		
66.	POLKA-DOT	RED		

	Bucket	Spinner	W	L
67.	GREEN	BLUE		*
68.	YELLOW	BLUE		*
69.	RED	ORANGE		*
70.	RED	ORANGE		*
71.	POLKA-DOT	RED		*
72.	GREEN	POLKA-DOT		*
73.	BLUE	BLUE	*	
74.	BLUE	STAR		*
75.	GREEN	YELLOW		*
76.	BLUE	BLUE	*	
78.	GREEN	YELLOW		*
79.	BLUE	ORANGE		*
80.	BLUE	POLKA-DOT		*
81.	ORANGE	GREEN		*
82.	GREEN	RED		*
83.	PLAID	GREEN		*
84.	ORANGE	ORANGE	*	
85.	STAR	GREEN		*
86.	YELLOW	BLUE		*
87.	YELLOW	BLUE		*
88.	GREEN	BLUE		*
89.	GREEN	POLKA-DOT		*
90.	POLKA-DOT	STAR		*
91.	BLUE	GREEN		*
92.	BLUE	BLUE	*	
93.	ORANGE	YELLOW		*
94.	BLUE	BLUE	*	
95.	PLAID	GREEN		*
96.	RED	RED	*	
97.	POLKA-DOT	GREEN		*
98.	BLUE	RED		*
99.	GREEN	BLUE		*
100.	GREEN	BLUE		*

A Teacher's Comments

Each student in this group received the total of 9 points possible on their game design. Their rules were clear and easy to understand, their model was neat, they correctly concluded that the game would make a profit, and the game was easy to construct and use.

Susy received 12 of the 13 points possible for her written report. Her descriptions of why people would want to play the game and why this game should be chosen are somewhat general; for this I deducted 1 point. I also commented that Susy makes a small error in adding the results of the experiments (where she reports the total winning as —11090— rather than —11050—), but I did not deduct for this error.

Heidi received 9 of the 13 points possible for her written report. I deducted 1 point for her comment that, from the group's experiments, the experimental probability of winning is approximately 5.5 out of 100 games, because this does not match the given data. Heidi gives the correct expected payout but she doesn't explain how she calculated it; 1 point was deducted for this. Another point was deducted because, although Heidi describes the data collection and presents the results, she does not connect that information to the probability of winning the game or the expected payout. A fourth point was deducted because of the effort the reader must expend to follow Heidi's report.

Unit Project

The Carnival Game

This project requires you to use the mathematics you have studied in several units, including this one. You will make a game for a school carnival and test your game. Then, you will write a report about your game.

Part 1: Design a Carnival Game

You can design a new game or redesign one of the games you analyzed in this unit. Keep these guidelines in mind.

- The game should make a profit for the school.
- The game should be easy to set up and use at a school carnival. It should not require expensive equipment.
- The game should take a relatively short time to play.
- The rules should be easily understood by people your age.

Part 2: Test Your Game

After you have drafted a game design, play the game several times until you feel confident that you can predict what will happen in the long run. Keep track of your trials, and include that information in your report.

Part 3: Submit Your Design to the Carnival Committee

Once you are satisfied that your game is reasonable, prepare to submit your design. Your submission to the committee should include two things: a model or a scale model of the game and a written report.

Unit Project The Carnival Game **61**

Notes _____

_____

_____

_____

Model or Scale Model

If you build a scale model instead of an actual model, give the scale factor from the scale model to the actual game.

You can either construct the model out of similar materials to those you would use for the actual game, or you can prepare scale drawings of the game. If you make drawings, be sure to include enough views of your game so that anyone could look at the drawings and construct the game.

Report

Include a set of rules that explains how the game is played, how much it costs to play, how a player wins, and how much a player wins.

Part 4: Write a Report

Write a report about your game to the carnival committee. Assume that the committee consists of teachers in the building (not just mathematics teachers), parents, and other students. Your report should include:

- The experimental probability of winning the game that you found from playing the game several times. If possible, give the theoretical probability as well. If you don't give the theoretical probability of winning your game, explain why you did not.

- The amount of money the school will collect and how much they should expect to pay out if the game is played many times. Explain how you determined these amounts.

- An explanation of why your game should be chosen. Explain why the game is worth having in the carnival and why you think people would want to play it.

Notes _____

_____

_____

_____

Looking Back and Looking Ahead

Unit Review

In this unit, you studied some basic ideas of probability and some ways to use those ideas to solve problems about probability and expected value. In particular, you studied how to

For: Vocabulary Review Puzzle
Web Code: anj-7051

- find and interpret experimental and theoretical probabilities
- use simulations to gather experimental data
- use tree diagrams, and other listing techniques to find all of the possible outcomes
- use area models in which probabilities are shown as parts of a whole square or circle

Use Your Understanding: Probability Reasoning

To test your understanding and skill with probability ideas and strategies, consider the following problem situations.

1. Maria's homework problem is to design two dartboards that match these conditions:

   - The probability of landing in region A is 30%.
   - The probability of landing in region B is 25%.
   - The probability of landing in region C is 20%.
   - The remaining space on the dartboard is region D.

   a. Draw a square dartboard that meets the given conditions.

   b. Draw a circular dartboard that meets the given conditions.

   c. For each dartboard, find the probability that a dart will

   i. land in region D

   ii. land in a region other than D

   iii. *not* land in region A

Notes _____

_____

_____

_____

2. Gabrielle and Jim are playing the Match/No Match game. On each turn, the players spin the two spinners shown below. Gabrielle scores 1 point if the spins match, and Jim scores 1 point if they do not match.

 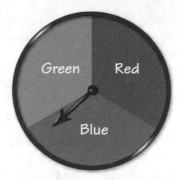

   a. Use a tree diagram to show all the possible outcomes for this game.

   b. What is the theoretical probability of getting a match?

   c. What is the theoretical probability of getting a non-match?

   d. Does each player have an equally-likely chance of winning?

   e. Is this a fair game? If so, explain why. If not, explain how you could change the rules to make it fair.

3. Kali and Antonio designed a new computer game. They programmed the game so the probability that a player will win is $\frac{1}{4}$ on each turn. If the player wins, the score increases by four points. If the player loses, two points are deducted from the score.

   a. Matthew plans to play 12 rounds of the game. How many points can he expect to score?

   b. How many points per round can Matthew expect to win or lose?

   c. Is this a fair game? If not, how would you change the points won or lost so that it is a fair game?

Notes _____

_____

_____

_____

Explain Your Reasoning

When you use mathematical calculations or diagrams to solve a problem or make a decision, it is important to justify your reasoning. Answer these questions about your work.

4. What does it mean to say that the probability of an event is $\frac{1}{2}$ or $\frac{2}{3}$ or $\frac{5}{8}$?

5. How are experimental and theoretical probabilities of an event related to each other?

6. Explain and illustrate with specific examples how you could use each strategy to analyze probabilities.

    a. tree diagrams   **b.** area models

7. What does it mean to find the expected value of a chance activity with numerical outcomes? Give three examples of problems in this unit for which you had to find the expected value.

Look Ahead

You will almost certainly meet the ideas about probability of this unit in future study and problem solving in mathematics, science, and questions about games of chance. These are the basis of statistical reasoning that will be developed in the *Connected Mathematics* unit, *Samples and Populations,* and which you will see in areas as diverse as genetics, the payoffs in state lotteries, and local fundraisers.

Looking Back and Looking Ahead   **65**

Notes _____

_____

_____

_____

A

area model A diagram in which fractions of the area of the diagram correspond to probabilities in a situation. For example, suppose there are three blue blocks and two red blocks in a container. If two blocks are drawn out, one at a time, replacing the block drawn each time, the area model below shows that the probability of getting two red blocks is $\frac{4}{25}$.

Area models are particularly helpful when the outcomes being analyzed are not equally likely, because more likely outcomes take up larger areas. Area models are also helpful for outcomes involving more than one stage, such as rolling a number cube, then tossing a coin or choosing a bag, then drawing a block from it.

modelo por áreas Un diagrama en el que las fracciones del área del diagrama corresponden a las probabilidades en una situación. Por ejemplo, si hay tres bloques azules y dos bloques rojos en un recipiente y se saca un bloque cada vez sin reemplazarlo, el modelo por áreas de abajo muestra que la probabilidad de sacar dos bloques rojos es $\frac{4}{25}$.

Los modelos por áreas son especialmente útiles cuando los resultados que se analizan no son igualmente probables, porque los resultados más probables tienen áreas más grandes. Los modelos por áreas son también útiles para resultados que incluyen más de un paso, como tirar un cubo numérico y luego tirar una moneda, o elegir una bolsa y luego sacar un bloque de ella.

Second Choice

		B	B	B	R	R
	B	BB	BB	BB	BR	BR
	B	BB	BB	BB	BR	BR
First Choice	B	BB	BB	BB	BR	BR
	R	RB	RB	RB	RR	RR
	R	RB	RB	RB	RR	RR

B

binomial probability The probability of getting one of two outcomes (like heads or tails).

probabilidad binomial La probabilidad de obtener uno de dos resultados (como cara o cruz).

E

equally likely Two or more events that have the same probability of occurring. For example, when you toss a fair coin, heads and tails are equally likely; each has a 50% chance of happening. Rolling a six-sided number cube gives a $\frac{1}{6}$ probability for each number to come up. Each outcome is equally likely.

igualmente probables Dos o más sucesos que tienen la misma probabilidad de ocurrir. Por ejemplo, cuando se lanza una moneda "justa" la probabilidad de obtener cara es igual a la de obtener cruz; es decir, cada caso tiene una probabilidad del 50%. Tirar un cubo numérico de 6 lados supone $\frac{1}{6}$ de probabilidad de que salga cada número. Cada resultado es igualmente probable

66 What Do You Expect?

Notes _____

_____

_____

_____

expected value (or long-term average)

Intuitively, the average payoff over the long run. For example, suppose you are playing a game with two number cubes. You score 2 points when a sum of 6 is rolled, 1 point for a sum of 3, and 0 points for anything else. If you roll the cubes 36 times, you could expect to roll a sum of 6 about five times and a sum of 3 about twice. This means that you could expect to score $(5 \times 2) + (2 \times 1) = 12$ points for 36 rolls, an average of $\frac{12}{36} = \frac{1}{3}$ point per roll. Here, $\frac{1}{3}$ is the expected value (or average over the long run) of one roll.

valor esperado (o promedio a largo plazo)
El promedio de puntos o la recompensa conseguidos tras realizar muchos intentos. Por ejemplo, imagínate un juego con dos cubos numéricos en el que obtienes 2 puntos por una suma de 6, 1 punto por una suma de 3 y 0 puntos por cualquier otra suma. Si lanzaras los cubos numéricos 36 veces, sería de esperar que obtuvieras una suma de 6 aproximadamente cinco veces y una de 3 aproximadamente dos veces. Es decir, cabría esperar conseguir $(5 \times 2) + (2 \times 1) = 12$ puntos en los 36 lanzamientos, o sea un promedio de $\frac{12}{36} = \frac{1}{3}$ punto por lanzamiento. Aquí $\frac{1}{3}$ es el valor esperado (o promedio a largo plazo) de un lanzamiento.

experimental probability
A probability that is determined through experimentation. For example, you could find the experimental probability of getting a head when you toss a coin by tossing a coin many times and keeping track of the outcomes. The experimental probability would be the ratio of the number of heads to the total number of tosses, or trials. Experimental probability may not be the same as the theoretical probability. However, for a large number of trials, they are likely to be close. Experimental probabilities can be used to predict behavior over the long run.

probabilidad experimental
La probabilidad determinada mediante la experimentación. Por ejemplo, para hallar la probabilidad experimental de obtener cara en el lanzamiento de una moneda, podrías efectuar numerosos lanzamientos y anotar los resultados. Dicha probabilidad sería la razón entre el número de caras y el número de lanzamientos, o intentos. La probabilidad experimental puede no ser igual a la probabilidad teórica. Sin embargo, es probable que estén muy cerca durante muchos lanzamientos. Las probabilidades experimentales sirven para predecir lo que ocurrirá a largo plazo.

F

fair game
A game in which each player is equally likely to win. The probability of winning a two-person fair game is $\frac{1}{2}$. An unfair game can be made fair by adjusting the scoring system, or the payoffs. For example, suppose you play a game in which two fair coins are tossed. You score when both coins land heads up. Otherwise, your opponent scores. The probability that you will score is $\frac{1}{4}$, and the probability that your opponent will score is $\frac{3}{4}$. To make the game fair, you might adjust the scoring system so that you receive 3 points each time you score and your opponent receives 1 point when he or she scores. This would make the expected values for each player equal, which results in a fair game.

juego justo
Un juego en el que cada jugador tiene igual probabilidad de ganar. La probabilidad de ganar en un juego justo entre dos personas es $\frac{1}{2}$. Para hacer justo un juego que no lo es, se puede ajustar el sistema de reparto de puntos o de recompensas. Por ejemplo, imagina un juego que consiste en lanzar dos monedas "justas". Si salen dos caras, tú obtienes puntos. Si no, los obtiene el otro jugador. La probabilidad de que tú consigas los puntos es $\frac{1}{4}$ y la probabilidad de que los consiga el otro jugador es $\frac{3}{4}$. Para hacer justo el juego, podrías ajustar el sistema de reparto de puntos de manera que, cada vez que salgan dos caras, tú recibas 3 puntos y en las demás ocasiones el otro jugador reciba 1 punto. Esto haría que los valores esperados para cada jugador fueran iguales, lo que resulta en un juego justo.

English/Spanish Glossary **67**

Notes _____

_____

_____

_____

Law of Large Numbers This law states, in effect, that as more trials of an experiment are conducted, the experimental probability more closely approximates the theoretical probability. It is not at all unusual to have 100% heads after three tosses of a fair coin, but it would be extremely unusual to have even 60% heads after 1,000 tosses. This is expressed by the Law of Large Numbers.

Ley de números grandes Esta ley enuncia, en efecto, que cuantos más intentos de un experimento se realizan, más se aproximará la probabilidad experimental a la teórica. No es inusual tener 100% caras después de tres lanzamientos de una moneda justa, pero sería extremadamente inusual tener incluso 60% de caras después de 1,000 lanzamientos. Esto se expresa con la Ley de números grandes.

O

outcome A possible result. For example, when a number cube is rolled, the possible outcomes are 1, 2, 3, 4, 5, and 6. Other possible outcomes are even or odd. Others are three and not three. When determining probabilities, it is important to be clear about what the possible outcomes are.

resultado Consecuencia posible. Por ejemplo, cuando se lanza un cubo numérico, los resultados posibles son 1, 2, 3, 4, 5 y 6. Otros resultados posibles son pares o impares. Otros son es tres y no tres. Cuando se determinan las probabilidades, es importante definir cuáles son los resultados posibles.

P

payoff The number of points (or dollars or other objects of value) a player in a game receives for a particular outcome.

recompensa El número de puntos (o dólares u otros objetos de valor) que recibe un jugador por un resultado particular.

probability A number between 0 and 1 that describes the likelihood that an outcome will occur. For example, when a fair number cube is rolled, a 2 can be expected $\frac{1}{6}$ of the time, so the probability of rolling a 2 is $\frac{1}{6}$. The probability of a certain outcome is 1, while the probability of an impossible outcome is 0.

probabilidad Un número comprendido entre 0 y 1 que indica la probabilidad de que ocurra un suceso. Por ejemplo, cuando se lanza un cubo numérico justo, se puede esperar un 2 cada $\frac{1}{6}$ de las veces, por lo que la probabilidad de que salga un 2 es $\frac{1}{6}$. La probabilidad de un suceso seguro es 1, mientras que la probabilidad de un suceso imposible es 0.

R

random Outcomes that are uncertain when viewed individually, but which exhibit a predictable pattern over many trials, are random. For example, when you roll a fair number cube, you have no way of knowing what the next roll will be, but you do know that, over the long run, you will roll each number on the cube about the same number of times.

sucesos aleatorios Aquellos sucesos cuyos resultados, al considerarse separadamente, no son seguros, pero que podrían presentar un patrón previsible al observarse a lo largo de muchos intentos. Por ejemplo, en el caso de lanzar un cubo numérico perfecto es imposible saber cuál será el resultado del próximo lanzamiento; sin embargo, sí se sabe que a la larga saldrá cada uno de los números del cubo numérico aproximadamente la misma cantidad de veces.

S

sample space The set of all possible outcomes in a probability situation. When you toss two coins, the sample space consists of four outcomes: HH, HT, TH, and TT.

espacio muestral El conjunto de todos los resultados posibles en una probabilidad. Cuando lanzas dos monedas, el espacio muestral son cuatro resultados: CC, CX, XC y XX.

Notes

theoretical probability A probability obtained by analyzing a situation. If all of the outcomes are equally likely, you can find a theoretical probability of an event by listing all of the possible outcomes and then finding the ratio of the number of outcomes producing the desired event to the total number of outcomes. For example, there are 36 possible equally likely outcomes (number pairs) when two fair number cubes are rolled. Of these, six have a sum of 7, so the probability of rolling a sum of 7 is $\frac{6}{36}$, or $\frac{1}{6}$.

probabilidad teórica La probabilidad obtenida mediante el análisis de una situación. Si todos los resultados de un suceso son igualmente probables, entonces para hallar la probabilidad teórica del mismo se escribe una lista de todos los resultados posibles y luego se halla la razón entre el número de resultados que produce el suceso deseado para el número total de resultados. Por ejemplo, al lanzar dos cubos numéricos perfectos existen 36 resultados igualmente probables (pares de números). De ellos, seis tienen una suma de 7, por lo que la probabilidad de obtener una suma de 7 es $\frac{6}{36}$, o sea, $\frac{1}{6}$.

tree diagram A diagram used to determine the number of possible outcomes in a probability situation. The number of final branches is equal to the number of possible outcomes. The tree diagram below shows all the possible outcomes for randomly choosing a yellow or red rose and then a white or pink ribbon. The four possible outcomes are listed in the last column. Tree diagrams are handy to use when outcomes are equally likely.

diagrama de árbol Un diagrama que se utiliza para determinar el número de resultados posibles en una situación de probabilidad. El número de ramas finales es igual al número de resultados posibles. El siguiente diagrama de árbol muestra todos los resultados posibles al escoger al azar una rosa amarilla o roja, y luego una cinta blanca o rosada. Los cuatro resultados posibles aparecen en la última columna. Los diagramas de árbol son útiles cuando los resultados son igualmente probables..

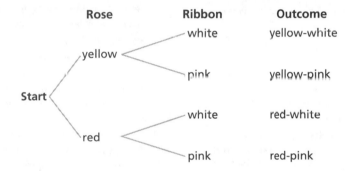

Notes _____

_____

_____

_____

Academic vocabulary words are words that you see in textbooks and on tests. These are not math vocabulary terms, but knowing them will help you succeed in mathematics.

Las palabras de vocabulario académico son palabras que ves en los libros de texto y en las pruebas. Éstos no son términos de vocabulario de matemáticas, pero conocerlos te ayudará a tener éxito en matemáticas.

D

describe To explain or tell in detail. A written description can contain facts and other information needed to communicate your answer. A diagram or a graph may also be included.
related terms: express, explain

Sample: A 5 results in three of ten rolls of a number cube. Describe the theoretical and experimental probability of rolling a 5.

> Since a number cube has six equal sides and the number 5 appears once, the theoretical probability of rolling a 5 is $\frac{1}{6}$. The experimental probability of rolling a 5 is $\frac{3}{10}$.

describir Explicar o decir con detalle. Una descripción escrita puede contener hechos y otra información necesaria para comunicar tu respuesta. También se puede incluir un diagrama o una gráfica.
términos relacionados: expresar, explicar

Ejemplo: Tres veces sale un 5 de 10 tiros de un dado numérico. Describe la probabilidad teórica y experimental de que salga un 5.

> Como un cubo numérico tiene seis caras iguales y el número 5 aparece una sola vez, la probabilidad teórica de que salga un 5 es $\frac{1}{6}$. La probabilidad experimental de que salga un 5 es $\frac{3}{10}$.

determine To use the given information and any related facts to find a value or make a decision.
related terms: solve, evaluate, examine

Sample: Eugene's favorite shirts are red, black, orange, and white. His favorite hats are red, gold, and black. Eugene randomly selects one shirt and one hat. Make a chart to determine the probability that they are the same color.

> The chart shows 12 possible combinations. The probability of the same color is $\frac{2}{12}$, or $\frac{1}{6}$.
>
> **Hats**
>
> | Shirts | R | G | B |
> |---|---|---|---|
> | R | RR | RG | RB |
> | B | BR | BG | BB |
> | O | OR | OG | OB |
> | W | WR | WG | WB |

determinar Usar la información dada y cualesquiera datos relacionados para hallar un valor o tomar una decisión.
términos relacionados: resolver, evaluar, examinar

Ejemplo: Las camisetas favoritas de Eugene son rojas, negras, anaranjadas y blancas. Sus sombreros favoritos son rojos, dorados y negros. Eugene selecciona al azar una camiseta y un sombrero. Haz una tabla para determinar la probabilidad de que sean del mismo color.

> La tabla muestra 12 combinaciones posibles. La probabilidad de que sean del mismo color es de $\frac{2}{12}$ ó $\frac{1}{6}$.
>
> **Sombreros**
>
> | Camisetas | R | D | N |
> |---|---|---|---|
> | R | RR | RD | RN |
> | N | NR | ND | NN |
> | A | AR | AD | AN |
> | B | BR | BD | BN |

70 What Do You Expect?

Notes _____

_____

_____

_____

design To make using specific criteria.

related terms: draw, plan, outline, model

Sample: Nils invented a computer game which randomly hides a treasure chest. The probability that the treasure chest will be hidden in the sand is 50%, in the water 30%, in the rocks 10%, or in the grass 10%. Design a computer screen that Nils could use for his game.

I'll draw 50 of the 100 square units as sand, 30 as water, and 10 each as rocks and grass to match each probability.

diseñar Hacer siguiendo un criterio específico.

términos relacionados: dibujar, planear, bosquejar, modelar

Ejemplo: Nils inventó un juego de computadora que aleatoriamente esconde un cofre lleno de tesoro. La probabilidad de que el cofre esté escondido en la arena es del 50%, en el agua del 30%, en las rocas 10% o en el pasto del 10%. Diseña una pantalla de computadora que Nils pudiera usar para su juego.

Dibujaré 50 de los 100 cuadrados unitarios para la arena, 30 para el agua, 10 para las rocas y 10 para el pasto, para representar cada probabilidad.

---

explain To give facts and details that make an idea easier to understand. Explaining can involve a written summary supported by a diagram, chart, table, or a combination of these.

related terms: describe, clarify, describe, justify

Sample: Find the probability of tossing a coin 3 times and getting heads exactly two times. Explain your reasoning.

I can use a tree diagram to look at all eight possible outcomes when tossing a coin three times.

Toss 1	Toss 2	Toss 3	Results
H	H	H	**HHH**
		T	**HHT**
	T	H	**HTH**
		T	HTT
T	H	H	**THH**
		T	THT
	T	H	**TTH**
		T	TTT

There are 3 outcomes in which there are exactly two heads. The probability is $\frac{3}{8}$.

explicar Dar datos y detalles que facilitan el entendimiento de una idea. Explicar puede requerir la preparación de un informe escrito apoyado por información basada en un diagrama, una tabla, un esquema o una combinación de éstos.

términos relacionados: describir, aclarar, justificar

Ejemplo: Halla la probabilidad de tirar una moneda al aire 3 veces y que caiga cara exactamente dos veces. Explica tu razonamiento.

Puedo usar un diagrama arborescente para observar los ocho resultados posibles al tirar una moneda al aire tres veces.

Tirada 1	Tirada 2	Tirada 3	Resultados
Ca	Ca	Ca	**CaCaCa**
		Cr	**CaCaCr**
	Cr	Ca	**CaCrCa**
		Cr	CaCrCr
Cr	Ca	Ca	**CrCaCa**
		Cr	CrCaCr
	Cr	Ca	CrCrCa
		Cr	CrCrCr

Hay 3 resultados en que hay exactamente dos caras. La probabilidad es de $\frac{3}{8}$.

Academic Vocabulary **71**

Notes _____

_____

_____

_____

Index

72 What Do You Expect?

Notes

Notes _____

_____

_____

_____

Acknowledgments

Team Credits

The people who made up the **Connected Mathematics 2** team—representing editorial, editorial services, design services, and production services—are listed below. Bold type denotes core team members.

Leora Adler, Judith Buice, Kerry Cashman, Patrick Culleton, Sheila DeFazio, Katie Hallahan, Richard Heater, **Barbara Hollingdale, Jayne Holman,** Karen Holtzman, **Etta Jacobs,** Christine Lee, Carolyn Lock, Catherine Maglio, **Dotti Marshall,** Rich McMahon, Eve Melnechuk, Kristin Mingrone, Terri Mitchell, **Marsha Novak,** Irene Rubin, Donna Russo, Robin Samper, Siri Schwartzman, **Nancy Smith,** Emily Soltanoff, **Mark Tricca,** Paula Vergith, Roberta Warshaw, Helen Young

Additional Credits

Diana Bonfilio, Mairead Reddin, Michael Torocsik, nSight, Inc.

Technical Illustration

WestWords, Inc.

Cover Design

tom white.images

Photos

2 t, David Young-Wolff/PhotoEdit; **2 b,** Comstock Images/Getty Images, Inc.; **3 foreground,** Russ Lappa; **3 background,** Bill Frymire/Masterfile; **5,** Lisette Le Bon/SuperStock; **9,** Richard Haynes; **14,** Jack Hollingsworth/Corbis; **17,** Russ Lappa; **28,** Peter Beck/Corbis; **32,** Stockbyte Royalty Free Photos; **40,** David Young-Wolff/PhotoEdit; **44,** Philip James Corwin/Corbis; **47,** Larry Williams/Corbis; **50,** Comstock Images/Getty Images, Inc.; **52,** Jed Jacobsohn/Getty Images, Inc.; **55,** Ron Kimball/Ron Kimball Studios; **56,** H. Reinhard/Masterfile ; **61,** Richard Haynes

Data Sources

The Don Calhoun data on page 38 is reprinted courtesy of Sports Illustrated: "Sports People: Don Calhoun" by Lisa Bessone, SI, April 26, 1993, Copyright © 1993, Time Inc. All rights reserved

The "Largest Hamster Litter on Record" data on page 56 is courtesy of Guinness World Records, Ltd.

Note: Every effort has been made to locate the copyright owner of the material reprinted in this book. Omissions brought to our attention will be corrected in subsequent editions.

Notes _____

_____

_____

_____

Labsheet 1.1

Match/No-Match

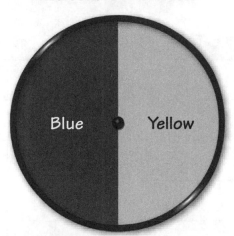

Turn #	Results	Player A's Score	Player B's Score
1			
2			
3			
4			
5			
6			
7			
8			
9			
10			
11			
12			

Turn #	Results	Player A's Score	Player B's Score
13			
14			
15			
16			
17			
18			
19			
20			
21			
22			
23			
24			

Labsheet 1.3

....

Multiplication Game

Roll Number	Product	Odd or Even
1		
2		
3		
4		
5		
6		
7		
8		
9		
10		
11		
12		
13		
14		
15		
16		
17		
18		

Roll Number	Product	Odd or Even
19		
20		
21		
22		
23		
24		
25		
26		
27		
28		
29		
30		
31		
32		
33		
34		
35		
36		

Labsheet 2.1

Making Purple

Spinner A

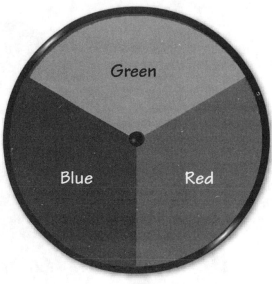

Spinner B

Labsheet 2.1

Making Purple

Spinner A

Spinner B

Labsheet 3.1

Nishi's One-and-One

Nishi's One-and-One

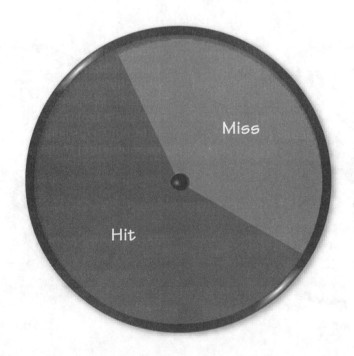

Labsheet 3.2

....

One-and-One Free Throws

20% free-throw percentage

P(0) _____

P(1) _____

P(2) _____

40% free-throw percentage

P(0) _____

P(1) _____

P(2) _____

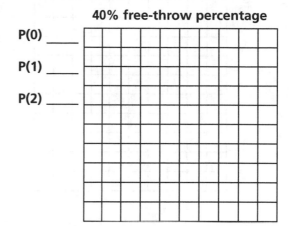

60% free-throw percentage

P(0) _____

P(1) _____

P(2) _____

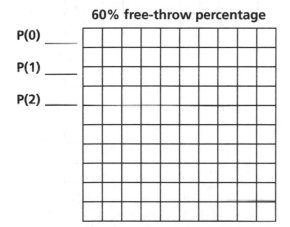

80% free-throw percentage

P(0) _____

P(1) _____

P(2) _____

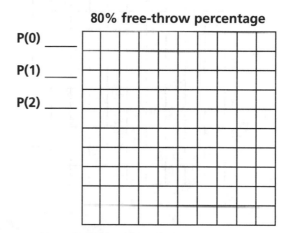

Free-Throw Average	P(0)	P(1)	P(2)	Expected Value
0%				
20%				
40%				
60%				
80%				
100%				

Hundredths Grids

PACING: _____

Mathematical Goals

_____

_____

_____

_____

Launch

_____

_____

_____

_____

_____

_____

_____

Materials

Explore

_____

_____

_____

_____

_____

_____

_____

Materials

Summarize

_____

_____

_____

_____

_____

_____

_____

Materials

A

area model A diagram in which fractions of the area of the diagram correspond to probabilities in a situation. For example, suppose there are three blue blocks and two red blocks in a container. If two blocks are drawn out, one at a time, replacing the block drawn each time, the area model below shows that the probability of getting two red blocks is $\frac{4}{25}$.

Area models are particularly helpful when the outcomes being analyzed are not equally likely, because more likely outcomes take up larger areas. Area models are also helpful for outcomes involving more than one stage, such as rolling a number cube, then tossing a coin or choosing a bag, then drawing a block from it.

Second Choice

		B	B	B	R	R
	B	BB	BB	BB	BR	BR
	B	BB	BB	BB	BR	BR
First Choice	B	BB	BB	BB	BR	BR
	R	RB	RB	RB	RR	RR
	R	RB	RB	RB	RR	RR

B

binomial probability The probability of getting one of two outcomes (like heads or tails).

E

equally likely Two or more events that have the same probability of occurring. For example, when you toss a fair coin, heads and tails are equally likely; each has a 50% chance of happening. Rolling a six-sided number cube gives a $\frac{1}{6}$ probability for each number to come up. Each outcome is equally likely.

expected value (or long-term average) Intuitively, the average payoff over the long run. For example, suppose you are playing a game with two number cubes. You score 2 points when a sum of 6 is rolled, 1 point for a sum of 3, and 0 points for anything else. If you roll the cubes 36 times, you could expect to roll a sum of 6 about five times and a sum of 3 about twice. This means that you could expect to score $(5 \times 2) + (2 \times 1) = 12$ points for 36 rolls, an average of $\frac{12}{36} = \frac{1}{3}$ point per roll. Here, $\frac{1}{3}$ is the expected value (or average over the long run) of one roll.

experimental probability A probability that is determined through experimentation. For example, you could find the experimental probability of getting a head when you toss a coin by tossing a coin many times and keeping track of the outcomes. The experimental probability would be the ratio of the number of heads to the total number of tosses, or trials. Experimental probability may not be the same as the theoretical probability. However, for a large number of trials, they are likely to be close. Experimental probabilities can be used to predict behavior over the long run.

F

fair game A game in which each player is equally likely to win. The probability of winning a two-person fair game is $\frac{1}{2}$. An unfair game can be made fair by adjusting the scoring system, or the payoffs. For example, suppose you play a game in which two fair coins are tossed. You score when both coins land heads up. Otherwise, your opponent scores. The probability that you will score is $\frac{1}{4}$, and the probability that your opponent will score is $\frac{3}{4}$. To make the game fair, you might adjust the scoring system so that you receive 3 points each time you score and your opponent receives 1 point when he or she scores. This would make the expected values for each player equal, which results in a fair game.

L

Law of Large Numbers This law states, in effect, that as more trials of an experiment are conducted, the experimental probability more closely approximates the theoretical probability. It is not at all unusual to have 100% heads after three tosses of a fair coin, but it would be extremely unusual to have even 60% heads after 1,000 tosses. This is expressed by the Law of Large Numbers.

O

outcome A possible result. For example, when a number cube is rolled, the possible outcomes are 1, 2, 3, 4, 5, and 6. Other possible outcomes are even or odd. Others are three and not three. When determining probabilities, it is important to be clear about the possible outcomes.

P

payoff The number of points (or dollars or other objects of value) a player in a game receives for a particular outcome.

probability A number between 0 and 1 that describes the likelihood that an outcome will occur. For example, when a fair number cube is rolled, a 2 can be expected $\frac{1}{6}$ of the time, so the probability of rolling a 2 is $\frac{1}{6}$. The probability of a certain outcome is 1, while the probability of an impossible outcome is 0.

random Outcomes that are uncertain when viewed individually, but which exhibit a predictable pattern over many trials, are random. For example, when you roll a fair number cube, you have no way of knowing what the next roll will be, but you do know that, over the long run, you will roll each number on the cube about the same number of times.

sample space The set of all possible outcomes in a probability situation. When you toss two coins, the sample space consists of four outcomes: HH, HT, TH, and TT.

theoretical probability A probability obtained by analyzing a situation. If all of the outcomes are equally likely, you can find a theoretical probability of an event by listing all of the possible outcomes and then finding the ratio of the number of outcomes producing the desired event to the total number of outcomes. For example, there are 36 possible equally likely outcomes (number pairs) when two fair number cubes are rolled. Of these, six have a sum of 7, so the probability of rolling a sum of 7 is $\frac{6}{36}$, or $\frac{1}{6}$.

tree diagram A diagram used to determine the number of possible outcomes in a probability situation. The number of final branches is equal to the number of possible outcomes. The tree diagram below shows all the possible outcomes for randomly choosing a yellow or red rose and then a white or pink ribbon. The four possible outcomes are listed in the last column (Figure 1). Tree diagrams are handy to use when outcomes are equally likely.

Figure 1

	Rose	Ribbon	Outcome
	yellow	white	yellow-white
		pink	yellow-pink
Start	red	white	red-white
		pink	red-pink

Index

INDEX

Acknowledgments

Team Credits

The people who made up the **Connected Mathematics 2** team—representing editorial, editorial services, design services, and production services—are listed below. Bold type denotes core team members.

Leora Adler, Judith Buice, Kerry Cashman, Patrick Culleton, Sheila DeFazio, Richard Heater, **Barbara Hollingdale, Jayne Holman,** Karen Holtzman, **Etta Jacobs,** Christine Lee, Carolyn Lock, Catherine Maglio, **Dotti Marshall,** Rich McMahon, Eve Melnechuk, Kristin Mingrone, Terri Mitchell, **Marsha Novak,** Irene Rubin, Donna Russo, Robin Samper, Siri Schwartzman, **Nancy Smith,** Emily Soltanoff, **Mark Tricca,** Paula Vergith, Roberta Warshaw, Helen Young

Additional Credits

Diana Bonfilio, Mairead Reddin, Michael Torocsik, nSight, Inc.

Technical Illustration

Schawk, Inc.

Cover Design

tom white.images